# Praise for
# *The Way of the Tiger*

If you are searching for an unusual place for possible solutions to your problems try a visit to Lance Secretan's zoo. A stimulating novel and seminar to nurture a new attitude to life and work.

*Doug Ackhurst,* Vice-President
Telemedia Communications Ontario Inc.

On the face of it a touching fable; in depth a powerful model and practical statement on eliciting greatness. Creative, practical, thought-provoking and empowering—difficult to put down.

*Dennis S.J. Shackel,* Professor of Education
University of Toronto

A unique approach highlighting the three keys to survival today: the customer, your people and leadership. This non-businesslike fable is written in a very user-friendly way.... I urge you to invest in the future of your organization and your people by buying every member of your team a copy.

*William P. Sutton,* Managing Director
Canadian Management Centre

Lance Secretan and a Ghost Tiger named Moose

have come up with a remarkable collaboration: *The Way of the Tiger* unleashes a wealth of usable management information in a most entertaining package.

*V.S. Maidman*, President
Equifax Canada Credit Information Services

A zoo—the perfect milieu for a fable about corporate culture.

*Gerry Schwarz*, President
Onex Corporation

This is a new breed of management book that is sure to make the reader a roaring success.

*Calvin J. White*, General Manager
Metropolitan Toronto Zoo

A very different and interesting approach.

*Tom Callaghan*, President
Dielcraft Furniture

Most business books I have read tend at some point to become very dull and slow, not so *The Way of the Tiger*. I read it with great enjoyment.

*Eric Morris*, President
Grote Manufacturing Ltd.

Like a rare trophy find, *The Way of the Tiger* leaps out of the dense underbrush of management literature.

*Herman M. Smith*, President
Herman Smith International Inc.

Reading *The Way of the Tiger* gave me the feeling that hope was indeed still inside Pandora's box.

*Rena Blatt*, Ministry of Municipal Affairs
Ottawa

Pipe dreams? Secretan smokes them. There is love in his life and life in his work.

*Wilder Penfield III*
Toronto *Sun*

Humorous and entertaining, *The Way of the Tiger* provides insight and an important message for all who work in bureaucracy.

*Larry Little*, President and CEO
Saskatchewan Housing Corporation

Lance Secretan's use of the fable makes this an easy book to read. The concepts make it a powerful learning experience.

*George Heaton*, Principal
George Heaton & Associates

I found *The Way of the Tiger* to be an innovative and

fun way to stress the linkage of corporate culture to quality of customer care to corporate success.

*Al Tolstoy*, Vice President, Western Region
Bell Cellular Inc.

A witty and original approach to excellence in the managerial process.

*John Gillespie*, President and CEO
Goliger's Travel

*The Way of the Tiger* is a successful book because, by being allegorical, it leads the reader into insights about the importance of particular management styles. It is effective in raising awareness of the people side of any and every business.

*Ken D. Cross*, Partner
Clarkson Gordon

# THE WAY
# OF THE
# TIGER

# THE WAY OF THE TIGER

## GENTLE WISDOM FOR TURBULENT TIMES

**LANCE H.K. SECRETAN, PhD**

Stoddart

Published in 1989 by
Stoddart Publishing Co. Limited
34 Lesmill Road
Toronto, Canada
M3B 2T6

---

CANADIAN CATALOGUING IN PUBLICATION DATA

Secretan, Lance H.K.
    The way of the tiger

Previous ed. published under title: The masterclass.

ISBN 0-7737-2355-2

1. Organizational effectiveness.    2. Management.
I. Title.

HD38.S42 1989      658      C89-094188-2

---

Cover Design: Brant Cowie/ArtPlus Limited
Printed and bound in the USA

# Contents

**THE FIRST KEY: Mastery**

THE SECOND KEY: **Chemistry**

**THE THIRD KEY: Delivery**

# Acknowledgments

 eldom is a creative work crafted by one individual alone, especially a book that breaks all the traditional rules of design, style and message. It is a confluence of MASTERY, CHEMISTRY and DELIVERY.

*The Way of the Tiger* is the result of intensive collaboration by people with a shared vision. The original concept has been shaped and reshaped by the unselfish contributions of a committed few.

Tricia Sheppard provided creativity, insights, feedback, encouragement and inspiration throughout this project. Whether her help flowed from our discussions during car journeys, on skiing trips, at breakfast or in the wee hours of the morning, she has made this book richer and, more importantly, she has enriched me, too. Her gift is love and LOVE is what this book is all about.

As a former university professor teaching Entrepreneurship, I enjoyed a unique privilege: selecting the most talented of my students to work for me. Robert V. Kozinets fit this bill perfectly, becoming my research assistant, laboring tirelessly to add to and correct biological, zoological, geographical and natural history facts as well as philosophical and psychological concepts. Much of his original material has been woven into the fabric of the fable.

Writers dream of editors like Donald G. Bastian. He doggedly untangled my prose so that it could be read by humans. Not only is he a brilliant wordsmith, but he is also the consummate politician and critic, always finding the successful, Machiavellian route to our goals and delivering criticism that makes you feel even better afterward than you did before. Remarkable gifts! I am also grateful for the staunch support of Angel Guerra, David Walmark, Portia Leggat and Sally Tindal at Stoddart Publishing.

Many of the concepts in *The Way of the Tiger* were polished by participants in scores of my workshops and seminars throughout the world. Denis Shackel uses this book as the core text in his course on the psychology of education for graduate teachers at the University of Toronto. My seminars with him and his students, their feedback and positive criticism and, more than anything, the joy of watching them fan the flames of their passion for teaching were a special gift for me.

George Heaton of George A. Heaton and Associates and Bill Sutton of the American Management

Association/Canadian Management Center, Anne Popma of the Whistler Center for Business and the Arts and Al Nicholson of WestRock Management supported the early Masterclass Retreat Programs. Dave Blair, president of D.C. Blair and Associates; Alan Harman of Scotia Mcleod Limited; John Myser, former president of 3M Canada and now vice president of the 3M Company, Minneapolis–St. Paul; Peggie Pelosi, vice president of Jocuse Inc.; Don Rumball, the former editor of *Small Business* magazine; Dr. Michael Rosenbush, managing partner, Right Association; and Gerry Schwartz, president of Onex Capital Corp., offered valuable feedback on early drafts.

Peter McLean wrote a fabulous song celebrating the fable, inspiring our collaboration on a musical version of the book for the stage. Chris Dedrick mastered the digital recording for the multi-media, scripted version.

At the Metro Toronto Zoo, Calvin White, general director, Toby Styles, manager of public relations and marketing, and John Carnio, curator of mammals, answered many silly questions and provided unrestricted access to archives and facilities. I also made friends with many of the volunteers and keepers there.

Susan Neath has been my administrative anchor, without whom I would probably have disappeared into a bureaucratic vortex.

Barbara Sheppard prepared original artistic suggestions, which helped set the tone for the illustrations by David Shaw.

Any mistakes, of course, are my own. It was fun making them!

Lance H.K. Secretan, PhD
Cataract, Ontario
Canada

# Mastery

Life's like a play: it's not the length but the excellence of the acting that matters. *Seneca*

Whatsoever thy hand findeth to do, do it with thy might. *Ecclesiastes 9:10*

# Chemistry

Friendship is a single soul dwelling in two bodies. *Aristotle*

A friend may well be reckoned the masterpiece of nature. *Emerson*

# Delivery

"Let me light my lamp," says the star, "and never debate if it will help to remove the darkness." *Rabindranath Tagore*

"Understanding human needs is half the job of meeting them." *Adlai Stevenson*

**The Dialogue** / IN WHICH *The Author discourses with Moose, the Ghost Tiger, at the Metro Zoo, and a book is born.*

uch of my life has been spent in the cockpit of high performance businesses, such as Drake International in its early pioneering years and Manpower Limited, which we built from zip to $100-million in ten years. And during the past few years, I have been directing a flourishing group of my own companies. The "rush" of entrepreneurship has been like riding a motorcycle through an art gallery, leaving little time for introspection. Usually any moments of self-analysis have been devoted to learning how and why my actions and those of my team differed when we were effective from when we were not. From these intermittent deliberations emerged a philosophy of leadership which I called Managerial Moxie, a kind of entrepreneur's touchstone. It seemed so suspiciously simple that I asked a network of successful executives to run interference on my hypotheses. They not only corroborated them but also offered their encouragement. The result was my book *Managerial Moxie: A Basic Strategy for the Corporate Trenches.*

*Managerial Moxie* is designed to help executives identify and apply the winning techniques of successful, entrepreneurial managers. The principles include:

- Developing a clear sense of purpose.
- Setting a climate for success.
- Building a motivating machine.
- Hiring top guns.
- Delegating.
- Corporate networking.
- Keeping close to the Customer.
- Using sparse controls.

This message has since been preached in many lands to as many heathens as have been willing to be converted!

The commercial success of *Managerial Moxie* drew me into teaching, lecturing, training and consulting, from which I continue to learn. One of the most penetrating lessons was the identification of a major oversight in my original message. In my seminars I frequently heard the cry, "It's *their* job to manage!" I would respond that managing and leading is not just the exclusive responsibility of *them*! It's not the special prerogative of some gray, faceless, bureaucratic hierarchy! For example, every one of the one hundred uniquely skilled members of a world-class symphony orchestra must exert leadership. Each achieves excellence by simultaneously playing both team and leadership roles. These principles of leadership hold true for any successful organization, whether it's an orchestra, a family, a government department or YOU: A TEAM OF ONE. It's even true for a Zoo!

## ZEN AND THE ART OF WORKING AND LIVING

I visit Zoos often. I find them wondrous places where reflection and contemplation of the great issues of work and life come easily. The creatures there appear to possess a certain knowing as they watch You watching them. They seem to practice Zen and the art of working and living.

The modern Zoo provides a powerful metaphor for work and life. It consists of a group of managers, scientists, professionals, volunteers and administrators—and thousands of creatures. Few of the one-hundred million North Americans who visit Zoos every year realize what goes on behind the scenes in efforts to stem the tide of ecological destruction. One hundred acres of rain forest are being destroyed every minute of the day and one animal species, usually an invertebrate, disappears every hour. Research, education, conservation and the successful Zoo-breeding of endangered species are all efforts to slow the destruction and over-exploitation of the animal habitat. A child transfixed in fascination by a newborn Lion cub or laughing at the Monkeys grooming each other may have no idea of the collaboration that has made these entertainments possible.

And what about the creatures? If You should have any doubts that the denizens of a world-class Zoo really do try very hard to perfect their skills, develop bonds with fellow residents and please Customers, or if You feel that a Zoo does not represent a true analogue for the kind of organization in which most of us would like to work, let me tell You a story that may convince You otherwise.

It happened in October 1983. The annual meeting of the American Association of Zoo Keepers was being held in Toronto. One of the many visitors to the Metro Toronto Zoo was Joe, the Gorilla keeper from the Lincoln Park Zoo, Chicago. On this particular day, Joe, a big man with a beard, was just one of the many others visiting the Gorillas in the Africa Pavilion. In the Metro Toronto Zoo, the Gorillas are separated from visitors by a floor-to-ceiling wall made from three-inch armored glass. The Gorillas can smell almost nothing and hear very little from behind this glass. Joe was off duty, so he was wearing sports clothes rather than his customary uniform. Two rows of regular visitors were in front of him.

The Gorillas were sleeping. Suddenly, one of the Gorillas stirred and spotted Joe. She did a double-take, ambled over to the glass to get a better view and stared into Joe's face. Two others followed suit. The three Gorillas stood tippy-toed with their noses pressed to the glass, staring at Joe for five minutes before boredom settled in. What communication took place? What was the transmission between Man and Mammal? What signals from humans could the Gorillas so readily read? Can we learn such perspicacity?

Zoo-People will tell You that this sort of thing happens over and over again throughout the world. To suggest that we are separated by our superior intellects and do not share common purposes, objectives and communications may be just one more example of human arrogance. It is important that we set aside our prejudices in order to consider fresh ideas objectively.

At the Metro Toronto Zoo there resides a Ghost Tiger called Moose—and that's his real name! Ghost Tigers, or White Tigers, as they are sometimes called, are uncommon. Their coloration, which may range from white to orange, is the result of recessive genes. A newborn Ghost Tiger will have received a recessive (white) gene from its mother and another from its father. The ghost effect is rare among Tigers; there are about fifty of these magnificent creatures in North America and only some one hundred and fifty worldwide. The effect is more common in Leopards, but in their case the recessive gene is nearly always black. A Leopard with a recessive gene is completely black and we usually call it a Panther.

All Ghost Tigers in Zoos have descended from one male, Mohan. He was a Bengal Tiger captured in Rewa, India, in 1951. Ghost Tigers in North America can trace their lineage to Mohini, Mohan's daughter, who is now a member of the National Zoo in Washington, D.C. Moose was born in 1981 and Kivali, Moose's mate at the Metro Toronto Zoo, in 1982.

Late one sunny summer afternoon, I was musing with Moose and explaining to him that I was working on a new book. As we talked, I tested my thoughts with him. I mentioned my belief that modern leadership should be based on three elegant and deceptively simple keys—the principles of success in work and life:

**THE KEY OF MASTERY: Undertaking whatever You do, in both Your personal and professional life, to the highest standards of which You are capable.**

**THE KEY OF CHEMISTRY: Relating so well with others on a personal and social level that they actively seek to associate themselves with You.**

**THE KEY OF DELIVERY: Finding Customers, both internal and external, identifying their needs and meeting them.**

"These three concepts of Mastery, Chemistry and Delivery," I told Moose, "represent a recipe for positive rhythm on Planet Earth. These Three Keys," I continued fervently, "are so powerful that they could put fire and passion into organizations, families and individuals, turning them into motivational engines of entrepreneurship and beauty and filling lives with joy."

Moose was much more interested than his laconic listening style suggested. He responded with a very pithy observation: "The organizational dynamics of Zoos, which we call 'Zoo-Communities,' resemble those of any other enterprise. Metro Toronto Zoo employs two hundred and thirty staff and more than four thousand animals, like me, who make them look good." That's when he first reached me with one of his inscrutable smiles.

We both stared pensively into the still waters of his pool for a few moments.

I wanted to press my theories further. "For centuries the pyramid structure has been the prism through which Western society has viewed all organizations—families, governments, corporations, charities—all our organized human groupings.

Known alternatively as the 'command-and-control' structure, it was first developed by the Chinese and then perfected by the Roman Catholic Church and the armies of the world. We have borrowed, improved and expanded the use of these techniques. We have adapted modern "organizational development" not only to the contemporary corporate organization but also to the family and to the individual in such personal matters as goal-setting and career planning. But the familiar, traditional pyramid structure has been with us for less than a thousand years, and modern management science, the glue which binds this model, only emerged one hundred and fifty years ago. In this short time we have barely begun to learn the basic techniques." I paused for Moose's reaction.

"But it doesn't matter," he said after a moment of reflection, "because most of those techniques are becoming obsolete and it's time to move on again. One hundred years ago, more than half Your human population worked independently on the land or in the arts and professions. By the late 1950s, this pattern had been completely reversed with three-quarters of Your working population 'going to work' as part of centralized manufacturing, government and administrative workforces. Although Your manufacturing output is rising rapidly, it is estimated that Your manufacturing employment will decline to less than ten percent of Your workforce by the year 2000. A massive downsizing, decentralizing and restructuring of modern organizations is occurring while, at the same time, individual members of Your society have become increasingly well-educated and autonomous." Moose was a perceptive observer of sociodemographic trends.

We sat silently. What social and organizational effects has this created? I wondered. Perhaps we need look no further than to the Fortune 500 companies for our answer: they employ three million fewer middle managers than they did seven years ago. Organizations have reacted by changing from the pyramid structure to an hourglass structure, a structure without middle managers. But the change has been so rapid that even this structure is becoming obsolete. What is taking its place? A "snowman" structure. The snowman organizational structure is a dispersed service organization (we are all, in one form or another, service organizations) with few top managers and fewer middle managers. The bulk of the employees are "implementers": sales and service staff who deliver services and products that meet Customer needs.

Since the majority of employees are implementers, they must now motivate, lead and appraise themselves. But little emphasis is given to motivation, leadership and self-appraisal in our educational system. Educators favor the "left-hemisphere," scientific subjects of the MBA program.

The decentralization of work and decision-making, the dramatic rise in self-employment and the transference of work to the home is blurring the lines between "work" and "play." The management of organizations, families, companies, governments and countries and the leadership of their members are making necessary a new set of rules based on personal responsibility and the empowerment of the individual.

I could feel Moose reading my mind. "So how are we to generate excellence, leadership, creativity, renewal, improvement, quality and self-esteem without a means for these crucial subjects to be learned?" he asked.

"By returning to a few core values which will yield a sense of economic, commercial and, therefore, spiritual renewal," I replied.

"For instance?" he challenged me. Like every great teacher, Moose had the knack of teaching by listening; he was forcing me to pull the answers from within.

## FOCUSING ON STRENGTHS

"Well," I began, "one of the most important tasks of any leader is to capitalize on the strengths of followers. This is most effectively achieved by developing their strengths while rendering their weaknesses irrelevant.

"But all too often we over-focus on our weaknesses and through our excessive urges to correct them, we create unnecessary stress and frustration for individuals. We are urged by colleagues and social convention to study, read and practice, so that those areas where we are less effective may be improved."

"Doesn't some emphasis on weakness have merit, especially when the weaknesses concerned are part of a strength?" Moose asked, putting me on the defensive.

"Yes," I replied.

But the Zoo-guru supported my proposition. "An old Turkish proverb states that 'One arrow does not bring down two birds.' If we have one arrow, it should be aimed at our strengths, not our weaknesses. The spirit soars, at work or play, when we practice and improve our strengths. Doing what we already do well, even better, yields an ever-deepening sense of self-esteem and joy."

## CONTINUING IMPROVEMENT—KAIZEN

Moose raised himself onto his haunches and looked at me quizzically. "Humans are understandably captivated by the stunning breakthroughs of these hi-tech times. But why do You not give equal value to the genius of incremental improvements?''

Moose had a point. He continued, ''In an outstanding book called *Kaizen: The Key to Japan's Competitive Success*, Masaaki Imai has shared with us a magical idea: *Kaizen*. Kaizen is a Japanese term which means 'gradual, unending improvement, doing *little things* better; setting—and achieving—even better standards.'

''In both our personal and corporate lives,'' Moose added, '''different' is not the only way; 'better' yields great progress, too.''


## PEOPLE AND THINGS

I started a new train of thought. ''You know, Moose, as a former professor I identify with Thomas Hart Benton's observation: 'Who can really feel comfortable in this culture now except maybe a few guys who are good at mathematics?' Teaching at a leading university business school, and presiding over several companies, I have enjoyed a unique insight into both the academic and 'real' worlds. The core courses (those You *must* take) in the MBA program at one of Canada's leading business schools are:

*Financial Accounting for Managers, Microeconomics for Management, Introduction to Administrative Statistics, Behavioral Components of Organiza-*

*tions, The Environmental Framework of Management, Introduction to Management Accounting, Macroeconomics for Management, Introduction to Finance, Operations Management, Marketing Management, Organization Analysis, Strategy Formulation and Implementation and Strategy Study."*

Moose registered his disdain with a chuckle. "But out of thirteen of those courses, seven are rooted in finance or statistics and not people," he pointed out. I was beginning to find Moose's intellectual precision uncanny. "Precisely," I continued, "and during my seminars, I often ask participants what courses they would prescribe if they could re-design the MBA program to equip tomorrow's leaders for the real world of work. They usually suggest such subjects as:

*Communications, Listening, Writing, Perception, Empathy, Identifying Opportunities, Leadership, Motivation, Recruiting, Inspiring, Delegating, Customer Sensitivity, Responsibility and Taking Initiative.*

"Sometimes they even recommend Zen and Shakespeare as required texts, too! What You may have noticed is that we teach managers, at home and at work, the science of how to *manage things*; but what successful, experienced managers know is that we

must also teach the art of *leading people*. As Ross
Perot said, 'Inventories are managed; people are
led.' "

We discussed these concepts a while longer before
I revealed one of my concerns. Fifty-five thousand
new English book titles were being released in the
Canadian market each year. Standing in front of the
rows of books in any bookstore, they all seem to look
the same and seem to carry the same messages.
How could I communicate our ideas in a totally
unique way, writing a book like no other, one that
would capture the imagination of the reader? I mentioned Marilyn Ferguson's view that the brain learns
best from stories, that people are moved by metaphors, drama and symbols.

Moose agreed, pointing out that Einstein once
said, "The most beautiful experience we can have is
the mysterious. It is the fundamental emotion that
stands at the cradle of true art and true science."
Moose said I should follow that advice in writing my
book. Then he made another brilliant suggestion. He
proposed that we work on the new book together. I
was both stunned and delighted.

## "YOU"
"Let me make another suggestion," said Moose. "If
we write a fable about work and life it should cele-

brate the idea of 'You,' the Customer. 'Customers' are those who depend upon us to meet *some* of their needs. In this sense employees, friends, clients and family are all each other's 'Customers' in life. You, the Customer, are the heart of any organization, any family, in fact, any group in our society. It is important that we put Your needs first, because everything starts with You, depends on You and requires me to collaborate with You! I am on *Your* payroll! You, the Customer, are the reason for our existence! You are entitled to respect! Without You we have no Zoo-Community, no Customers and no purpose. Without You, my client, my supplier, my competitor, my colleague, my supervisor, my friend, my family, my lover, there is no team, no celebration, no point! Without You, I would be reduced to . . . '*i*.' In our new book let us signal the importance of You by commencing the words 'You' or 'Your' and 'Customer' with a capital letter."

"Excellent idea!" I agreed.

We were making tremendous progress. It would be an exciting project. We shared a contemplative silence again. Then Moose said, "You know, Lance, the two metaphors that most commonly come to mind when we attempt to encourage excellence and outstanding performance are *war* and *sport*. We exhort our children and our colleagues to 'annihilate the competition' by 'blowing them out of the water' or 'cleaning their clocks.' The ruling ethos seems to be Vince Lombardi's famous epithet, 'Winning isn't everything; it's the only thing.' The driving conceptual forces behind this attitude are conflict and hostility, which lead to the 'zero-sum game': what I win, You lose, while the size of the pie remains the same. Beauty contests, ball games, nuclear war, chess, corporate politics and market-share in finite markets are all zero-sum games."

"You're right Moose," I replied. "Excellence in our society is less a product of conflict and hostility than of collaboration—the combined efforts of a committed team. In such collaborations, the tasks of *managing and leading* each other and *finding and keeping Customers* are shared by all. This is what organizations with legendary reputations for quality, service and value have already learned. Simply put, the difference between whether an organization is mediocre or superb is determined by whether *all* its individual members are mediocre or superb. The more we decentralize, the more we become dependent on the competence and human-relations skills of the individual. The airline fails us when the reservation clerk does. The hotel chain fails us when the front desk staff do. The orchestra fails us when a musician does. By collaborating we can create a bigger pie, a 'positive-sum game.' "

"We all share the load, the opportunity and the responsibility," added Moose. "It's the same for a church, a hospital, a family, a university or even a country—*it's even the same for a Zoo.*"

## LOVE AT HOME AND WORK

"In my readings, Moose, I have found that many great teachers, Christ, Lao-tzu and Buddha among them, have urged us to love one another in two ways. The first is unconditional—'Love is, above all, the gift of oneself,' was how Jean Anouilh put it. The second is love given in a spirit of enlightened self-interest: 'The love we give away is the only love we keep,' in the words of Elbert Hubbard. In the latter case, the message is that a consciously chosen, loving mindset is the most effective way to accomplish the dreams of humanity. It therefore follows that love is the golden thread which runs through successful organizations. Love means communicating, listening, respecting and not judging. *Great leaders inspire their followers through love.*"

"Now You are onto my favorite subject, Lance," said Moose enthusiastically. "Leadership is not restricted to designated superiors. Leadership flows from the minds of followers more than from the titles of leaders; more from the perception of willing followers than from an anointment. A leader is a person who loves his or her followers enough to spare no effort in their development, personal fulfillment and empowerment. Followers love their leaders enough to share their vision and dedicate themselves to its achievement. Leaders and followers help each other to create fun, joy and self-esteem, at home and at work. They go about their affairs with a 'caring eye.'

"As the twentieth century draws to a close, we are witnessing one of the most significant paradigm shifts of our time: the shift from the 'engineering paradigm' (people are skills to be managed and exploited) to the 'human paradigm' (people are principally motivated by the fulfillment of their own purposes). It is a paradigm shift which is reforging contemporary concepts of leadership, motivation and human development throughout Western society."

"Love is my favorite subject, too, Moose," I said quietly.

"Let's start writing our book which will be about love at work and in life," said Moose. Dusk faded into night and our collaboration began. The results await You on the pages that follow.

ONE / IN WHICH *We find Moose, the Head Cat and Zoo-Guru, preparing for the Masterclass he is to give the next day to Tamias the Chipmunk.*

oose rolled slowly onto his back and gazed at the sky. What a magnificent day! What a perfect sky! How wondrous and beautiful is the symmetry of life! He searched Heaven's ceiling for a cloud, but it was flawless. His eyes narrowed as they tracked closer to the sun. The rays created a dappled effect on his eyelashes. Moose recalled learning somewhere that this was how Albert Einstein had discovered the Theory of Relativity. Lying on a hill one summer day, the great scientist had wondered what it would be like to ride on one of those sunbeams. His wandering mind was drawn on a fantastic journey that defied his formal training in physics. Returning to the blackboard in his classroom, Einstein redefined the worlds of physics and mathematics in the process of explaining the non-rational truth he had imagined that afternoon.

"Now there was a mind!" reflected Moose approvingly. "If it is true that mankind uses a sparse one percent of the mind's potential, then Einstein probably used two percent regularly. I wonder what the average for our organization is? The Manager-People probably use one percent and the animals use two for an average of one and a half percent. That's fifty percent above average!"

Moose liked the Manager-People, but he felt they held an inflated view of their contribution to the Zoo-Community's success. He liked the Customer-People, too, and he suspected that there was a positive correlation between Manager-People spending less time in meetings and more Customer-People visiting the Zoo-Community. That's when he had formulated

**Moose's Law of Meetings: Customer satisfaction is inversely related to the amount of time spent in meetings.**

Moose scratched his ear. There were many more Customer-People here than in Cincinnati. He recalled his apprenticeship in Ohio. The Manager-People there had called him Roger (after a distant relative), but it's the tradition for the Zoo-Mentor and Head Cat to have a distinctive name. So just before he was transferred to Toronto he was renamed Moose. Not much of a name for an aristocratic Ghost

Tiger descended from the venerable Mohan! "There are only fifty of us in North America and they give me the name of an overgrown deer with a hat rack, a Roman nose, a beard and an overhanging lip! Why couldn't they have given me a beautiful name like my wife's: Kivali?" Moose flicked his tail in mild frustration. "Haven't they heard that the sweetest sound in any language is the sound of one's own name?"

But Moose had learned that it is unseemly for a Zoo-Guru to complain, even to himself. The Head Cat must always maintain a positive, philosophical outlook. As Zoo-Guru, he was the Dean of the Masterclass, the custodian of the Three Keys: Mastery, Chemistry and Delivery. Moose inspected his great paws absent-mindedly. He found that debates like this were best resolved between the Yin and the Yang of his two inner voices.

"So, in a position of such responsibility, I will put this pettiness aside," his Yang voice said with mock sophistication.

"Good job You weren't a Dog," Yin responded. "They'd have probably called You Rex or Fido! Or a Chipmunk. You'd've been Alvin!"

Moose's daydream suddenly evaporated. Chipmunk? Moose's crowded diary for next week flowed into his thoughts. Tomorrow was the first day of a new Masterclass and his first Tutorial was with a Chipmunk called Tamias. Judging from the briefing he had received, Moose's next protegé was intelligent and had a "can-do" attitude—the two most important criteria in any talent search. Experience had taught Moose that attitude and intelligence are the two greatest assets a team can acquire in an individual because, unlike skills, they can't be taught. Tamias would bring an excellent track record to the Zoo-Community.

Moose refocused his eyes and rolled over onto his stomach. He found that he could think better when he looked like a sphinx, and thinking was an essential part of the Mentor's advisory role. He found himself face to face with a small crowd of Customer-People who were observing him. He bathed in the warmth of a hundred joyful faces on this balmy summer Sunday. As he repaid the smiling Customer-People with his languid feline gaze, posing for the photographers and offering his best profile, he planned a learning odyssey for Tamias: a Masterclass.

TWO / IN WHICH *Tamias, in preparation for his Masterclass, meets Mandy the Mandrill, from whom he learns the meaning of Mission.*

he sun eased over the cedars, warming the gray meadows with its early gold. As the light inched towards the outcrops of granite at the forest's edge, Tamias munched a breakfast of sunflower seeds under his favorite dogwood tree. He liked life and life had been kind to him. He had enjoyed a fast-track career on the grounds of a multinational corporation, in the town's park, on a university campus and in the garden of a seniors' residence.

In many ways, his previous jobs had been enjoyable. But looking back, that's all they seemed to be: *jobs. This* day, however, was a red-letter day. In less than two hours Tamias would enroll in the Masterclass of the pre-eminent organization in the world of creatures: the Zoo-Community. Bill the Hairy Woodpecker had delivered the news by Morse code last week and Tamias's family and friends had been torn between envy and celebration ever since.

Membership in the Zoo-Community is by invitation only and is the universal ambition of every creature. Nomination alone is sufficient cause for congratulation.

Tamias had done his homework. He had researched his prospective fraternity with care, visited future colleagues and studied both Manager-People and Customer-People.

One experience had made a profound impact on him. In a visit to the Zoo-Community, as part of his preparation for his initial interview, he had struck up a friendship with Mandy, one of the Mandrills (the Purple-muzzled Baboons). During one of these discussions, Mandy had given Tamias an insight into the true Mission of the Zoo-Community. Pointing to a group of saucer-eyed youngsters, she whispered, "Watch their faces light up with smiles."

Then Mandy sauntered past Tamias towards the edge of the pond where her sister Jackie had paused for a drink. While Jackie scooped up water, one small handful at a time, Mandy scaled the Fiddle-leaf Fig Tree. It wasn't clear to Tamias whether or not Jackie was an accomplice in what happened next, but without warning, Mandy dropped out of the tree onto Jackie, body-checking her into the water. An eruption of laughter greeted a bedraggled Jackie as she

emerged from the pond. Shaking the excess mois-
ture from her fur, she surveyed the Customer-
People—a gaggle of smiles vibrating with glee.

But the show had only just begun. Jackie wheeled
her wet-slicked body across the enclosure, tearing
after Mandy, who kept but a Hare's-breadth in front
of her. As they hammed it up, happy smiles and
chortles billowed from their delighted audience.
Eventually, running out of steam, they settled in the
higher branches of the tree to groom each other
before resuming their serendipitous agenda.

Mandy rejoined Tamias. "You see, everyone here
knows the Zoo-Community's Purpose, our Mission.
We know Customer-People don't come here just to
see us. If that's all they wanted, they could go to
museums where they could get a closer look at
natural history. Do You know what our real Mission
is? *We sell smiles*."

Tamias listened intently.

"Work it out," Mandy continued. "The admission
price is six dollars. Each Customer-Person spends an
average of four hours visiting the Zoo-Community.
During that time we aim to get them smiling at least
once every four minutes, fifteen times an hour, sixty
times altogether. This works out to just a dime per
smile. That's the Customer need that we meet and
You've just seen how we ensure Customer service,
value and satisfaction." We have a theme song here:

*The Human Race wears a beautiful face*
*Which well you may see at the Zoo;*
*It's a better place for the populace*
*'Cos the critters there celebrate You!*

Then she was off, racing upside down across the sea of smiling faces.

Tamias revelled in the joy of his discovery. "A community of smile-givers, a Mission to make Customer-People happy. What a team to belong to!" He couldn't wait to meet Moose, the great Ghost Tiger, Head Cat and Mentor of the Zoo-Community. He was nervous—but ready.

amias scampered across the unsheltered expanse of open parking lot, pausing to catch his breath beneath the sign that read "Village Edge, Indo-Malaya Pavilion, Africa Pavilion." A sudden, piercing shriek, *"Kee-rah!"*, raised the stripes on his back. It also stirred the Black-winged Starlings who began whistling and clicking to each other. Tamias traced the trumpeting sound to the top of the sign.

"I'm Bah-rabar, which means 'Leader,' and I am Your Masterclass Guide during Your visit to the Zoo-Community."

"Pleased to meet You," said Tamias, trying to regain his composure as the Peacock gave his splendid tail-feathers an imperious flick.

"You are to follow me," Bah-rabar directed, as he dropped lightly to the ground.

It would be two hours before Customer-People thronged the pathways of the Zoo-Community. Until then Tamias could ignore the everyday hazard of human feet. As the two passed the Lion-tailed Macaques, Bah-rabar gave his bugle-call greeting again.

Tamias scampered down the Lion Trail behind Bah-rabar as the handsome Peacock strode past the Village Edge Building and across the boardwalk that spanned the wooded ravine. "Ghost Tigers," read the sign. Bah-rabar stopped. Tamias's heartbeat shifted into a higher gear.

"Tamias, let me offer You some advice that I think will serve You well during Your learning odyssey," said the Masterclass Guide. "I want You to pay particular attention to *Moose's Moxie*."

"What is *Moose's Moxie*?"

"Over the years, Moose has developed eleven Laws that are the foundation of his philosophy. He will share them with You. If You understand, believe and practice them, You will sail safely on the Great River of life."

"Thank You for the advice," said Tamias.

"Please take the Great Maple Tree down to the ravine floor. You will be received by Kivali. I will meet You here when You have finished Your first Tutorial with Moose."

FOUR / IN WHICH *Moose conducts Tamias's first Tutorial, teaching him the importance of meeting Customer-People's needs; the Three Keys of Mastery, Chemistry and Delivery; the Laws of Enlightened Self-Interest, Mission and Mastery; and his personal philosophy of learning.*

amias was wired with excitement as he approached his first meeting with the Zoo-Guru. Kivali was standing at the base of the Great Maple Tree to greet him. Even though Tamias had often heard of Kivali's beauty, the reality stunned him. The gaze from the blue centers of Kivali's green eyes was narcotic. Here stood one hundred and seventy white-furred kilos of power, finished with a pink smile.

"Welcome to our home," she purred, breaking his trance. Tamias scurried to keep up with Kivali, who was loping towards the building thirty meters away. These were the spacious quarters from which Moose and Kivali conducted the Masterclass.

As they passed through the large open door, Moose rose to greet them. Tamias was awed again. More than three meters long and weighing two hundred and seventy-five kilos, Moose was almost twice the size of Kivali. He was a feline machine of enormous grace and beauty. His square head was much larger than Kivali's and his whiskers black, not white. Tamias felt like a moth trapped by the candle of Moose's eyes.

> *In what distant deep or skies*
> *Burnt the fire of thine eyes?*

Having risen to greet his guest, Moose settled sleekly to the ground again. Kivali joined him.

"What kind of name is Yours?" asked Moose, scrutinizing his new pupil.

"My first name is Tamias, which means steward, or one who stores or takes care of provisions, and my last name is Striatus, which means striped," came Tamias's measured reply. He knew that the Masterclass had begun; he was being assessed.

"And what ends do You wish to serve by becoming a member of our Zoo-Community?" asked Moose with well-rehearsed detachment.

"Many of my friends are members and I've always envied the enjoyment they derive from their work, as well as their commitment to the Zoo-Community." It was a genuine observation, and Tamias awaited the Zoo-Guru's reaction.

Moose remained impassive, reflecting. "Here comes the big one," guessed Tamias.

"Have You formed an opinion as to the Mission, the Purpose of the Zoo-Community?" asked Moose.

Tamias started to answer but paused to let his brain catch up with his mouth, recalling his discussion with Mandy the Mandrill. He released each word with care: "*I think your Mission is to sell smiles. The members of the Zoo-Community are meeting Customer-People's needs through service, value and satisfaction.*" Tamias rarely sweated like this and his little pulse was racing.

Moose trapped Tamias again with his gaze. Not a sinew twitched on his sprawling frame. Tamias wrenched a glance at Kivali, but her eyes were as silent as emeralds.

Slowly, Moose's stern gaze melted. His whiskered jowls creased into a warm and welcoming smile.

"Tamias, our team is composed of four thousand individuals, just like You, who have learned that fun and rewards flow from collaboration and love. We are an organization in which size is measured by the heart, not by height, weight or power. Here we are committed to meeting the needs of Customer-People. By making them smile, we make ourselves smile. We try to be generous, by deferring, in order to achieve our own goals. Empathizing with the Customer-People's needs and wishes is the means by which we satisfy our own. This is known as

**Moose's Law of Enlightened Self-Interest: In order to receive from Your employer, You must first give to Your Customer."**

Moose continued, "If You learn well what we have to teach, You too will bathe in the beauty of kinship. Through our teachings we will give You the Three Keys to success in work and life. These keys— Mastery, Chemistry and Delivery—will open doors for You in the opposite way to most. Constant engagement of the Three Keys will bring bounteous material rewards. But constant pursuit of material rewards will only ensure that they remain elusive. This paradox is known as

**Moose's Law of Mastery: Mastery never seeks reward; rewards always find Mastery.**

This is the secret of excellence!"

Tamias was overjoyed and overwhelmed. Overjoyed because hidden in Moose's message lay the path of his acceptance into the Zoo-Community. Overwhelmed by the power of Moose's message. So sound. So eloquent. So exciting!

Tamias was silent for a moment. Then he phrased his ambition. "How do I become a member of the Zoo-Community?"

"Before You may become one of us, Tamias, You must learn the Three Keys—Mastery, Chemistry and Delivery—which together make up our philosophy. To help You do so, You have been assigned to Your own, personal Masterclass. You will be coached by some of the finest and most experienced Tutors in the Zoo-Community. But to hear them well, You must *listen*. 'Listen' and 'silent' share the same letters. To listen, truly listen, You must stop hearing Yourself and start listening to those who are speaking. In this way, You will become Your own teacher and Your Tutors will become Your facilitators. Do You follow me?"

Tamias nodded. "How would You advise me to prepare for my Masterclass?" he asked.

Moose looked at Kivali, silently inviting her to respond.

"You must listen with Your eyes first and Your ears second," she offered. "Some things, like being in love, can never be described as well as they are experienced. And don't intellectualize Your learning experience, just do it. When You don't think about it, You will do it best."

Moose nodded his concurrence. "When You are with Your Tutors," he said, "look into the faces of

Customer-People, especially the very young and the very old. The joy You will find there is the reason why more Customer-People visit Zoo-Communities around the world each year than all spectator sports added together. We are the world's largest class-room. This joy is our purpose. I call this

**Moose's Law of Mission: The only Purpose of organizations is to meet Customers' needs.**

"I hope that through Your Masterclass You will come to understand how we have achieved such high stand-ards in our lives and our work. If You learn the Three Keys, You, in turn, will be equipped to play Your role in our future."

Moose paused. Kivali and Tamias remained silent. After a moment Moose inquired, "Are You ready for Your first class?"

Tamias rubbed his restless nose nervously. "Yes!" he replied.

"Good!" said Moose, rising to indicate the end of their first meeting. "You will learn the Three Keys to success in work and life during my Masterclass. This consists of a number of classes taught by experts in their fields which You and I will review in our tutorial together.

"Take the Great Maple Tree to the Boardwalk," Moose continued, "where Bah-rabar is waiting for

You. Your first classes are dedicated to the principles of Mastery, and to that end, we have assigned some of our finest Masters to You. First, Bah-rabar will guide You to Lenny and Holly Gibbon, our Master Arboreal Gymnasts. Later, Bah-rabar will introduce You to Brunel Beaver, the Master Marine Engineer and Dam Builder. Your final class of the day will be with Raja and Rani Hornbill, our Masters in Parenting and House Building. At sundown, Bah-rabar will return You here for a quiet drink at our poolside. We will then discuss the experiences of Your first day in our Masterclass.''

# The
# First
# Key

## *Mastery*

Undertaking whatever You do, in both Your personal and professional life, to the highest standards of which You are capable.

FIVE / IN WHICH *Tamias meets Lenny and Holly the White-handed Gibbons, from whom he learns how to achieve Mastery through practice, modesty, interdependence, timing and fun.*

ah-rabar marched like a Cavalry Lieutenant decked out in ceremonial dress blues. He had discovered the short cut beneath the Boardwalk last year. Tamias was pleased that Bah-rabar would share this secret route between the Ghost Tigers' home and the Indo-Malaya Pavilion with him. He zigzagged in between the trees and the verge, pausing to watch the rocks dancing in the heat of the sun as he let Bah-rabar walk ahead. An American Goldfinch swooped through the air, lighting on a tall frond of grass, which bent to the ground under its weight. Tamias watched the Goldfinch kiss a Monarch butterfly in midair before it continued its undulating passes through the sedge.

Tamias caught up with Bah-rabar and assumed the lead as they branched down the Round the World

Trail to the Indo-Malaya Pavilion. Drawing a deep
breath, Bah-rabar signalled their arrival with a loud
*"Kee-rah!"* Tamias assumed that he would have to
get used to Bah-rabar's raucous communications.

"I'll wait for You here, little friend," Bah-rabar said
as Tamias slipped into the Indo-Malaya Pavilion.
*Friend!* Tamias was pleased with what he hoped was
Bah-rabar's way of encouraging their growing friendship.

Tamias's attention was caught by the Fire-bellied
Newts and the Malayan Boney-tongues. He'd never
seen them before.

"Hey, dude!" A baritone voice, sounding as if it had
been marinated in maple syrup, seeped into Tamias's
ears.

"Du-u-u-u-de!" Tamias searched for the source of
the rich sound. A Malayan Tapir opened one eye,
wiggled her stubby, movable trunk and slumped back
into her afternoon siesta. A Great Argus Pheasant
sized Tamias up, then resumed scratching irritably in
the dust.

"Yo, Chippo, up here."

Craning his head into the air, Tamias spied the
smiling face of Lenny, the White-handed Gibbon.

"I'm Lenny. How's it hangin', man?"

Tamias blinked.

"The leaves on the trees, Chippo," said Lenny with
a gurgling Gibbon laugh. "Come on up!"

Before Tamias could decipher the Gibbon's hip-speak, a white hand at the end of a long arm sped him like a high-speed elevator through the limbs of the Baobab Tree to the high bars of the Gibbons' home.

Tamias thought his poor heart had been left on the ground floor. If it hadn't, it probably had teeth-marks on it! Moose should have warned him about this. He had never dared to climb to such dizzy heights before. His Masterclass had taken a reckless turn! He tried to compose himself.

"The leaves are hanging just fine in the forest where I live, Lenny," he blurted nervously. "Allow me to introduce myself," he continued. "My name is Tamias and..."

"I know all that...how's it goin', Chippo?" the Gibbon said impatiently. "Gimme a high five, dude."

Tamias gave Lenny's hand a pat. The Gibbon laughed and spun through a *forward giant swing* on the high bar. Lenny's white face, hands and feet set off his dense, shaggy, sand-colored coat, giving him the air of a mime artist.

"You're all right, Chippo," Lenny said, returning with a *full twist dismount* and sliding next to him on the bars. "That arm-over-arm jazz is what we call 'brachiation,'" Lenny said, unable to conceal his pride. "We are the only folks who can do it!" He puffed his chest and gave Tamias a wink.

"Don't move Your buns, Chippo! The specs we got on You were pretty gnarly, and we aim to please, so we're gonna show You the show."

Without further ado, Lenny soared into the pavilion's peak by releasing his grasp and *hopping to pirouette*. Beams of light, which were being refracted from the sun, shone like spotlights on the rest of the Gibbon troop, who were silenced by their own concentration. "Ladies, Gentlemen and Your deeply honored guests, welcome to the acrobatic show of the century."

Tamias smiled. He loved the circus. How he wished his cousins, the Squirrels, could share this excitement. They often put on a stunt show for him. "In this corner, we have the beautiful and darin' Holly, who will perform feats with her three lovely sisters that will dazzle and amaze You. And in this corner," he motioned with his hand, "we have the Great Gibbono, who will walk the tightrope, teasin' fate and defyin' gravity. And I," he said, pausing for effect, "I will return to close the show, with a grand finale wherein I will perform a *quadruple flyin' backward somersault*, landin' in the arms of the lovely Holly."

With two *overhand grips* Holly stepped onto the upper bar. She stood momentarily in the spotlight, her beige coat shimmering with theater. With *three-quarter back giant swings* her sisters were beside her.

They used their arms, which were longer than their legs, to grip the bars as well. They undulated across the forest roof, arms alternating and legs dangling. Tamias had to turn his head so frequently, he felt like a ping-pong ball.

Holly was combining somersaults and leaps in a fluid pattern of aerial ballet. She seemed to ignore the reality of gravity. Landing lightly on her feet, she took a quick bow as Tamias applauded and gave the whistle for which Chipmunks are famous.

Then it was the Great Gibbono's turn. In a flurry of grips using all of his hands and feet, he soared to the top of the longest bar. He traversed it with his arms casually outstretched, with the same confidence You or I might have shown if it had been lying on the ground instead of hanging ten meters in the air.

Without warning, the Great Gibbono missed his grip and started to fall. Just as quickly, he recovered by turning in midair and catching the bar again with the other hand. He swung around under and then on top of the bar, and then, without any loss of timing or momentum, dropped ten meters to the ground. Looking at Tamias, he smiled and bowed.

Tamias applauded wildly with both relief and appreciation, wondering whether the accident was real or had been contrived to impress him. The Great Gibbono modestly made his way to the sidelines so that the next performers could take centerstage.

The Great Gibbono reminded Tamias of his cousin-once-removed called Sciurus, a Gray Squirrel who was generally recognized as one of the all-time tree-leaping greats. After one of his spectacular shows, Sciurus would sometimes find the time to share a few acorns with Tamias, exchanging tips or chattering and helping Tamias with his studies. Sciurus had taught Tamias an early lesson. Most often, he had said at the time, the greater the genius or accomplishment, the greater the modesty. Self-esteem grows with Mastery, thought Tamias. The Great Gibbono, it appeared to him, possessed that gentle humility of greatness.

A Shama Thrush swooped and soared in celebratory song and trilled a sentiment shared by Tamias:

> *"Alas for those who never sing,*
> *But die with all their music in them!"*

Lenny strode out onto the bar for his grand finale. He blew on both hands and saluted the anxious faces below him. Tamias wondered if his hands were permanently white from the constant use of chalk. Grabbing the bar with a *two-handed vise-grip*, Lenny slowly arched through a series of rotations, swirling faster and faster around the bar. With a triumphal cry, he released his grip, streaking through the air with a perfect *quadruple backward somersault*. Holly swung down from the bar, suspended by one hand, and caught Lenny with the other, cushioning the G forces before releasing her grip. The two dropped lightly to the forest floor, flexing their legs to soften the impact. They embraced in victory.

A moment of silent awe preceded the rapturous applause.

Tamias swelled with pride. He could feel the fur on the nape of his neck rising in excitement. They had, indeed, put on a wonderful show for him!

Moments later, Lenny came over to finish his conversation with Tamias, landing beside him with a *double back salto dismount*.

"Were You hip to what was shakin'?" he asked. Tamias marvelled at the cool professionalism, the way Lenny coped with the stress and excitement.

"I think so. . . ." Tamias replied uncertainly.

"You see, this was just a practice session, Chippo. We put on a bit of a mini-show for You today, man, but the real show goes on everyday. We have to work together as a team. It's part of Chemistry and we have to work at collaboration and synergy *every day*. We've gotta practice and practice and keep on practicin'. That's the only way the show ever gets put on at all. We make it look easy, but as a great coach once said: 'Practice doesn't make perfect; perfect practice makes perfect.'"

Tamias quickly caught the drift of Lenny's message. "Do You mean that You keep on practicing even when there's no one to watch, so that You'll do it even better next time?''

''Right on, right on!'' the Gibbon answered. ''Gimme another high five! Chippo, the hang is that if You wanna improve Your act, and we all wanna improve, You've gotta keep on doin' it again and again. Practice till You're perfect, that's what we Gibbons say. That's why we're the Masters of Acrobatics, because we keep on practicin' until everythin' is A-O.K. and right on all the way. Dig?''

Tamias nodded enthusiastically.

''That's cool,'' Lenny said. ''So You keep on practicin' whatever You do—on Your own time, You know—until Your act's together one hundred percento. Then You go out there and knock 'em dead, all the way. You readin' me, Chippo?''

''Yes, I am,'' replied Tamias thoughtfully. ''It's like a winning edge.''

''Right on target, Chippo my man. Hey, I gotta split now, Your ride's flaggin' me, but we'll hang together soon when You're a full-fledged member of the Zoo-Community. Catch You later.'' With a *forward hip circle* and *cast to handstand*, the tree-jockey rode the branches to another practice session with his friends.

Tamias sat up on his haunches, fantasies of achievement filling his thoughts. He would practice and visualize his goals of Mastery until he was as skilled and as proud as Lenny, Holly and the Great Gibbono.

SIX / IN WHICH *Tamias meets Brunel and Hoover the Beavers, from whom he learns that appropriate equipment, skills, knowledge, ability, understanding and simplicity lead to Mastery. He also learns the importance of mentoring.*

id You ever attend a Master-class, Bah-rabar?'' Tamias asked as they dodged through the Customer-People to the next class.

"Oh, yes!" Bah-rabar replied with fond recollec-tions. "Back then, Dinding the Orang-utan was the Zoo-Guru and he ran the Master-class. He's a philosophy scholar and he always used to fence with me about the consequences of Darwinism. Still tries to! Dinding was Moose's mentor."

Bah-rabar stopped, turning towards Tamias to address him with an important idea. "As a matter of fact, You may find this an interesting aspect of the next section of Your Masterclass. Brunel, the Bea-ver, Master Marine Engineer, Lodge Builder and Dam Constructor, spends a lot of time these days with an up-and-comer named Hoover. Brunel believes that Hoover, properly encouraged, may become even greater than he is. So Brunel has taken Hoover under his, er, wing, so to speak."

"Does everyone have a mentor?" Tamias asked.

"Everyone who *makes* it does," said Bah-rabar.

"And if they can't find one?"

"They won't make it!" Bah-rabar fanned his tail for one of the camera-toting Customer-People.

Tamias was shocked. Moose was his mentor during the Masterclass. But he didn't really have a long-term mentor. And he wanted to make it.

"How do I get one?" he asked anxiously.

"You have to be discovered."

"How do I arrange that?"

"There is a mentor for every student who loves to learn." Bah-rabar looked Tamias squarely in the eye. *"And we learn from those we love."*

Tamias wondered if Bah-rabar would consider being his mentor. He sensed a growing bond between them and he was beginning to like Bah-rabar very much. He hoped Bah-rabar would love him so that he would learn well.

But these thoughts didn't have time to crystallize. The Peacock was already marching towards the next rendezvous. They traveled across the meadows and through the woods until they reached the Americas Restaurant.

"Are You hungry?" Bah-rabar asked.

Until now, new ideas and faces, sights and sounds had crowded out thoughts of food. But Bah-rabar's question aroused Tamias's appetite. "Now that You mention it, I am a bit peckish!"

Bah-rabar flicked his crown in the direction of the picnic tables. "Customer-People eat their hamburgers here. They are careless with the sesame seeds from their buns. You should find all You want scattered on the ground for lunch. Let's allow about fifteen minutes?"

After satisfying their appetites they crossed the Round the World Tour Trail, quenching their thirst in the moat surrounding the Dall Sheep Mountain.

"We'd better go!" Bah-rabar said. "Brunel doesn't like to be kept waiting. Don't forget to listen for my call—we have one more class on today's agenda."

Tamias nodded his head and quickly climbed up and along the wooden slats of the veranda. The Snowy Owl was in the arms of Morpheus, oblivious to the Chipmunk scampering across the wire netting that covered her territory. Tamias made a brave leap onto an oak tree, using it as his elevator down to the edge of the Beavers' pond.

The Marine Engineering Seminar had already begun. He scaled the wall where he could enjoy a commanding view of the Beaver lodge, hoping not to be noticed.

"You must learn to appreciatize the *full* signification of things," Brunel Beaver was saying. "A tail is not *just* a tail. It's a *rudder* when You are swimmerizing. It's a *prop* when You are tree-cut-downing. It's a *counterweight* when You are transporterizing a load of mud, helping You to walk semi-erect. It's a *stabilizer* when You carry Your kits. It's a heated *nursing platform* for mothers when You are parentizing. It's an *alarm* when You slapperize it against the water surface. It *stores fat* for use during the lean winter period. When You sit on it, You reveal Your *unique dispenser* of castoreum which You use to make Your fur sleek and waterprooferized."

Brunel's voice rose a tone with each point, to which he gave additional punctuation by slapping his paddle-shaped tail on the water's edge. Rising on his hind legs and steadying himself with his tail, he concluded with a professorial flourish, "*A tail is not just a tail!* Get the picturization, Boy?"

Hoover nodded his head in vigorous acknowledgment.

The big Beaver paused, allowing his lesson to percolate before looking up at Tamias. "Come and join us!" he invited, his broad smile revealing four large, curved incisor teeth, colored bright orange.

Tamias lowered himself onto the roof of the lodge. The introductions were brief. "This is Tamias, a prospective member of the Zoo-Community." Hoover offered his fellowship.

Brunel turned back to Hoover. "You're not *just* going to constructuate dams, lodges and food caches. You will dis-rootificate large trees so that sun-loving, pioneer trees like Willow and Aspen, which easily seedify, will grow in their place. By this means, You will modify conifer and hardwood areas to create stands of faster-growing species that are more easily harvested. You will create wetlands that provide breederizing and feedifying grounds for Waterfowl, Fish, Salamanders, Frogs and Mammals such as Otter, Muskrats and Water Shrews.

"Your dams will control erosion, conserve water and increase the water quality of large rivers by reducing the amount of silt introduced. New species of plants that depend on the disturberations that You create will flourish in Your abandoned territories. Only the mighty Elephant modifies the landscape as much as we Beavers do! We are the movers and shapers!"

Brunel was on a roll. Hoover savored the wisdom. The Master Marine Engineer was weaving a spell. Although Tamias found Brunel a little long-winded and technical, he shared Hoover's reverence.

There seemed to be no end to Brunel's fervor. "You're not *just* a diver!" he exclaimed. "Diving doesn't just happen! First You have to have the right equipment. Hind feet that are webbified. Closability of nostrils. A rudder to steer with. Seal-tightable ear valves. Lips that seal Your mouth when You underwater-chewificate. Two protective flaps that close the back of Your mouth, preventing wood chips and water from entering Your throat. A transparent enclosure over Your eyes to protect them when You are below the surfature. Dense, sleeky fur and a specially adaptuated split toenail to comb the hair on the sides of Your body with waterprooferizing castoreum. A circulatory system that adjustifies through a diving reflex, slowing the heart, reducing blood circulation and conserving enough oxygen to allow You to remain submerged for fifteen minutes."

Brunel stopped to catch his breath. "Hoover, please enlighten me with Your opinion of what other factors must be present in a good diver."

Hoover had only seen two summers. His coat was lustrous and his jaw strong.

"Understanding and skill," he responded. "It's true that the right equipment is a prerequisite, but good equipment is worthless until it is harnessed to knowledge and ability. The combination is Mastery."

Brunel was pleased. Hoover had acquired a keen understanding of the deeper meaning of issues. He pressed his pupil: "To what purpose will You put Your understanding, skill and fine equipment?"

"Dam building."

"And what is the purpose of dam constructuation?"

"We are vulnerable on land but not in water. So we use, er, dam constructuation to back up waters, creating a shallow pond in which a lodge can be built a safe distance from the shore. It is easy for us to reach because we're strong swimmers, but it's virtually inaccessible to marauders."

Brunel smiled proudly, satisfied with the results of his tutelage. A keen mind was being honed. Lesser Beavers might have answered, "To constructuate our homes," or "To create a child-rearifying environment." But Hoover had reached beyond these ideas for a larger understanding.

"Tamias," said Brunel, "to the right equipment we must add understanding and skill. But we must also add simplicity. When we start constructuation of a new dam, we do it simply. We block-upify a small stream with sticks, stones, grass and mud to create a pond three to four meters deep. We only need to use the materials that are nearby. Block-upifying increases the waters, making them rise, which brings additional materials within easy reach. Thus, with relatively little extra effort, we can extenduate the initial project. We can continue this leveraging technique *ad infinitorum*.

"I've heard of lodges that have been in constant use for thirty years or more and dam complexifications extenduating more than three hundred and fifty meters in width. Simplicity, coupled with the technique of leveraging Your resources, can result in marvelous workifications."

"How do You leverage Your resources when You build a dam?" asked Tamias, not wishing to sound too ill informed.

"Well, as You may know, we constructuate a dam base of logs and stones, wedging sticks under the rocks, leaving the free ends tilting in the direction of the current. After weaving a latticework of brush, we scoop mud from the stream bed. Transporterizing it close to our chests while swimmerizing, we plaster the dam face.

"But, You see, we let nature do most of the hard work. For example, the sediment and debris transporterized downstream by the current serves to fillupify the crevices. Most of the trees we cut fall towards the side made heaviest by the greatest growth of branches. This is usually towards the pond because this is where the prevailing sunlightification encourages the most growth. The floor of the lodge is messified with wood chips from earlier meals which, in turn, create the drainage. This is how Beavers go with the flow. Get the picturization, Boy?"

"Yes. Yes, I do. Equipment, Understanding, Skill and Simplicity—the Zen of wetlands modification!" Tamias was rather pleased with his turn of phrase. But he didn't feel a need to respond further. Brunel and Hoover had made their points with great precision. There was little to be added.

But in the back of his mind, Tamias recalled homilies about the "busy Beaver" and maxims extolling the hard-working rodents and celebrating their industry. Was this a myth? Were Brunel and Hoover attempting to convey a different message?

As if he had been reading his mind, Brunel turned to Tamias and said, "A Master American poet once wrotified,

> *'From Beavers, bees should learn to mendify their Ways;*
> *A Bee just Works; a Beaver Workifies and Plays.'"*

Brunel and Hoover slipped into the pond. As Tamias stared at the two whirlpools they left behind, he reflected that the same poet had also written,

> *While Honey lies in Every Flower, no doubt;*
> *It takes a Bee to get the Honey out.*

SEVEN / IN WHICH *Tamias meets Nemesis the Serpent, who speaks for the stifling bureaucracy and resistance to change that exist in all organizations.*

A queasy
feeling
suddenly
came over
Tamias.
He felt
as if he
had been
drugged.
His legs
became
wooden
and
heavy.
Although
he tried to
keep
moving
forward,
an inexpli-
cable immo-
bility
had
overcome
him. "Tamias-
s-s!" Tamias
felt chilled as
he sat down to
take his
bearings. Who
had called his
name in
that
strange,
hissing
intona-
tion?

He turned to see what hidden force was preventing
him from leaving the Americas Pavilion. Then he saw
the Pit Viper, a deadly, banded coil of reddish brown
with slanted yellow eyes that locked onto Tamias.
One mean meter of Copperhead!

Tamias had a passing acquaintance with Snakes.
He had a healthy respect for many of them, too. At
home there were Brown Snakes, Red-bellied Snakes,
Garter Snakes and Smooth Green Snakes. Once his
brother had even been terrorized by a Massassauga
Rattler. But most of the Snakes Tamias knew had
different interests from the Chipmunk community
and their paths rarely crossed. When they had, he
had always been struck by their negative attitudes:
"pessimistic trouble-makers," his Dad had called
them. One winter, Tamias and his family had nearly
run out of food because Thamnophis the Garter
Snake had smooth-talked them into believing that the
winter ahead would be so mild as to make storing
provisions pointless.

But this Snake was different. Meaner.

"Good morning, Tamias-s-s. How nice to s-s-see
you! Allow me to introduce myself. My name is
Nemesis-s-s, and I am at your s-s-service. Please
call me Nem, all my friends around here do."

"Pleased to meet You, er, Nem." Tamias struggled
to hide his discomfort. "I'd love to stay but I am on

my way to meet the Hornbills and I don't want to be late."

"I've heard s-s-so much about you," hissed Nemesis. He spoke in a low voice with great deliberation. "I am told that you are s-s smart and s-s-studious. It is good to question and to be s-s-sceptical. All of us who have at heart the genuine interests of the Zoo-Community must always question the way things are."

Nemesis loosened his coils and slithered slowly towards Tamias, until he was pressed to the glass that separated them.

"Tamias-s-s, I like you, s-s-so I'm going to wise you up. Let me ask you a question. Do you think that Moose and Kivali are really that color? Of course not! The Manager-People s-s-stole their orange! They s-s-say that if the orange ever returns, Moose and Kivali will lose their power and that I, Nemesis-s-s, will become the Zoo Mentor! That's why Moose doesn't let me teach any part of the Masterclass. He fears for his power!"

Tamias was unprepared for this sinister conversation. "Why does he fear You?"

"Let me take you into my confidence, Tamias-s-s. I am planning a reorganization of the Zoo-Community. I would be very interested in the opinions you form during your Masterclass about how we do things around here. For example, our Zoo-Community covers two hundred and eighty-seven hectares, has four thousand members, representing more than four hundred and forty s-s-species. Each s-s-season, we eat one million kilograms of food. We give birth to one thousand new members every year. We have joined the ranks of the top ten Zoo-Communities in the world.

"But we s-s-still only employ fewer than three hundred Manager-People. We should s-s-start to behave like the large organization that we are. We're too informal. Everybody's on a first-name basis. We're too quick to change and not careful enough about rules, procedures and s-s-seniority. We s-s-should be more s-s-sensitive to our members' needs and pander less to Customer-People. We s-s-should hold more meetings to ensure that things are running well. After all, we are an important international organization, and we will never be respected unless we develop the s-s-structure that goes with our s-s-size and s-s-success.

"If I were in charge, these are s-s-some of the improvements that I would make. Would you like to help me make these advances, Tamias? If you feel, as I do, that it's time to s-s-strengthen our organization and improve order and discipline, I could use a keen administrative thinker like you! Would you like to be my top Lieutenant?"

Tamias was overwhelmed by the Serpent's seductive sermon. Many of Nemesis's ideas sounded so plausible. But Tamias wondered if his way was the best or only alternative.

"I have just spent time with Holly and Lenny the Gibbons and Brunel and Hoover the Beavers," Tamias observed. "They all demonstrated the power of Mastery. They have achieved remarkable efficiency through their skills. Why is Your approach better?"

"S-s-s-s-s!" Nemesis scoffed, arching his back. "I must compliment you on your incisive thinking, but Mastery is inconsistent and hard to manage and control. Order, formalization, proceduralization and s-s-systemization are the keys to continuing s-s-success. We all need clear rules that inform us exactly what is expected of us, reducing the uncertainties of jobs and making job classification easier."

Tamias nodded thoughtfully. Nemesis pressed even closer, lowering his voice and speaking still more softly. "I am in the process of building my team s-s-so that my power to introduce my ideas can be realized. Tamias-s-s, with you on my team we would revolutionize this place. Together we would become famous and the organization would be run in *our* interests. Will you please help me to do these good things for all the members of our Zoo-Community?"

Tamias reflected for a moment. "I will consider
Your ideas carefully as I complete my Masterclass,
and give careful consideration to Your interesting
proposal," he responded, trying to sound non-
committal.

"I would love to s-s-see you become part of the new
wave," Nemesis offered as a parting enticement.

Tamias hurried towards the exit. In almost all
respects, the philosophies of Moose and Nemesis
seemed opposed. He recalled something his Dad had
once said to him:

> *A Chipmunk with a sun-dial knows what time
> it is;*
> *A Chipmunk with two sun-dials isn't so sure.*

He slipped through the two sets of glass doors to
the outside of the Americas Pavilion. The Peacock
was waiting and watching Tamias. "You know you
have a friend in me. If I can help you at all with Nem's
and your plans, just let me know." He slipped into
the crowd.

Bah-rabar seemed different somehow, Tamias
thought. His look? His gait? The chemistry between
them? Tamias wasn't quite sure what it was. Almost
as if it wasn't Bah-rabar at all.

EIGHT / IN WHICH *Tamias meets Raja and Rani the Gray-cheeked Hornbills, from whom he learns that one achieves Mastery through pride, open-mindedness, self-development, networking, research and willingness to admit ignorance.*

ah-rabar re-emerged from the crowd of Customer-People, looking much more like himself. Even though Bah-rabar led the way, negotiating the Boardwalk through a stream of Customer-People proved to be a challenge for the Chipmunk. He quickly realized that he would achieve protection from their big feet most effectively by traveling the narrow ledge under the handrail. Once they were safely across the Boardwalk, the two used the Lion Trail to get to the Africa Pavilion, Bah-rabar striding ahead in a straight line, Tamias scampering in frequent zigzags. They passed the Family Center and the Africa Restaurant and then continued under the Monorail guideway. When they reached the Magnolia Tree, Bah-rabar stopped.

"I cannot go into the Pavilion. From here, You must proceed on Your own. As usual, be careful when You follow Customer-People through the doors. Inside You will find an open flight cage. Walk past the Sacred Ibis, the White-faced Whistling Ducks, the Spur-winged Plover, the Peach-faced Lovebirds and the Helmeted Turtle. When You reach the Black-footed Penguins, climb the Travelers Palm Tree where You will find Rani and Raja Hornbill waiting for You. Moose has allowed two hours for Your last class today."

Tamias slipped through the feet of the Customer-People as they unconsciously opened the double armored-glass doors for him. He paused to take in his surroundings. The Mozambique Mouthbrooders meandered lazily in the turgid waters of the moat beside him. The higher temperature and humidity made him feel short-winded. A chorus of squawks, shrieks, warbles and cries assailed his ears. He looked up. He was in the middle of a tropical rain forest under glass.

A unique hissing noise, like escaping steam, passed over his head. It was the sound of the wing-beats of the Gray-cheeked Hornbill. Alternating between bursts of flapping and gliding, with head stretched forward and feet trailing behind, Raja landed beside Tamias with the motion of a badminton birdie caught in a net. Raja was about half a meter long. Short black feathers covered his head, the front half of his body, wing tips and the ends of his tail. At the base of his large, triangular gray beak were two dark eyes surrounded by long, feathered eyelashes for which a Giraffe would have sold her soul.

"I'm Raja. You must be Tamias?" he asked breathlessly. Without waiting for a response, he continued: "This is a busy time for my wife, Rani, and me. Please don't think we are being sociopathic, but I hope You won't mind if we talk while we work?"

As if on a pogo stick, Raja bounced and hopped his way up to his attic. As their height increased, Tamias's pace slowed and his self-assurance ebbed. He definitely did not like heights. This was almost as bad as the rapid ascent he had made with Lenny. Unsteadily, Tamias secured himself in the fork of a lofty limb, ten meters above the ground. A box was fixed to a branch in the canopy of the rain forest and from it projected a perch. With a combination of hops and short bursts of flight, Raja landed on it. The only aperture was a tiny slit from which the tip of a sharp beak jabbed impatiently. Rani was inside. Raja began to shake his head vigorously until he had regurgitated a morsel for Rani, which he transferred to her beak.

"I don't want You to think of us as obsessive-compulsives, so there are one or two things that I'd like to explain," Raja said, keeping one eye on Rani's demanding beak and the other on Tamias. "We are

very keen Parents and our whole lives are controlled
by our offspring at this time of the year. They are on
their way!'' Raja beamed his paternal pride at
Tamias.

''Our children are our riches,'' said Raja over his
shoulder. Then his head became a blur as he produced another morsel for his imprisoned partner.
Raja replenished the beak several more times before
its demands subsided.

''We're pretty unique, Tamias,'' Raja resumed. ''We
Hornbills take great pride in our Parenting responsi-
bilities. I hope that we can share our Mastery of
Parenting with You.

''We don't believe in exposing our children to any
external risks during the formative portion of their
lives. For example, if any of our many enemies were
to discover their location, our children might suffer
psycho-traumatic shock or, worse still, severe physiological damage. So we have devised a Parenting
system that enhances their affiliative drives and pro-
tects them from predatory risks while avoiding the
fostering of any transient situational personality dis-
orders.''

Tamias stared at Raja and blinked. Should he admit
that he hadn't understood the last three sentences of
psycho-babble, or might this make him appear dim?
Perhaps this was a test—part of the Masterclass? He

weighed the alternatives for a moment and then decided to get the facts.

"Could You say that again, please, Raja?" Tamias asked. His tone indicated that although he understood perfectly, he would benefit from hearing it again in a different way.

"Oh! I am so sorry!" Raja replied. "I forget that some of our visitors are not social scientists or pediatrically fluent. I'll use shorter words! Are You familiar at all with the Parenting system that we have developed?"

"Well," said Tamias, "we bring up our children in the hollow of a tree or in a burrow about a meter below the ground. Perhaps You keep them in a safe place like that rather than in an exposed area like other birds?"

"You're absolutely right, Tamias. But we go one better. Instead of simply putting our children in a secret location, we take an extra precaution."

"And what is that?"

"We seal the entrance with the wife and children inside it!" Raja smiled, batting his over-sized eyelashes. "It's what Dr. Bird calls the Lock-in Method and it's been our Parenting system for thousands of generations. The Avian Psychologists have written articles about us and we have been interviewed and filmed many times. Rani and I even taught Parenting Skills 101 to the Pied Hornbills in the Indo-Malaya

Pavilion. And we do a lot of research. Research is what we are doing when we don't know what we are doing!"

The laughter that erupted from Raja in response to his own joke caused him to lose his balance. He flapped his wings furiously to avoid falling off his perch. Tamias permitted himself a private smile.

"Two moons ago, Rani's mud-gathering heralded nesting time. Two years ago, we were the first Gray-cheeked Hornbills to have offspring in any Zoo-Community in the Western Hemisphere." Raja paused to ensure that his audience was suitably impressed. "Rani started to pick up pellets of mud from our water hole. She made many trips to plaster the entrance to her nest until it was nearly closed. We worked as a team; she did the plastering and I got the meals." Another search for recognition. Tamias smiled in acknowledgment.

"After Rani had laid her three eggs, she finished walling-up the nest entrance with mud that had fallen inside. As You can see, all that is left is a narrow slit."

"Raja, I'm really impressed," said Tamias. "But the Lock-in Method must create a tremendous amount of work for You."

"Well, I'm making thirty-five trips a day until our chicks are hatched," Raja replied. "If it's anything like the last time, I'll be making seventy trips for the remaining twenty days."

Tamias thought about the numbers. He once had won a bet with his brother by getting eighty-four ragweed seeds into his mouth at one time! He sometimes made seventy trips a day to store the bulbs, seeds, fruit and nuts that made up the winter larder at home. He could appreciate the workload. "And how do You keep Your nest clean?" he asked.

"That's all part of our Parenting system. Rani passes all of the family's waste out to me through the slit. She even uses some of it inside to reinforce weaknesses in the plastering. We're very particular housekeepers."

"Isn't that a bit risky though? I mean, wouldn't littering the vicinity of Your nest alert Your enemies to Your location?"

"Ah!" said Raja, "we have thought of that. I take any of the waste that Rani passes out, and I fly away with it, scattering it as far from our home as possible to confuse our enemies!"

"How long is Rani walled up in her nest?"

"About twenty days of brooding and another twenty days of rearing," Raja responded. "During that time, she undergoes a complete molt and I hide her feathers a safe distance from the nest. As our children grow, the nest becomes crowded, so Rani builds a second story inside, supervising the children from the balcony. After forty days, she will peck away the seal. It's hard work for her; it's taken her as long as four hours before.

"After she leaves, the children start resealing the entrance immediately with their droppings and sticky berries and other items that I bring them. Rani relaxes for four days while I feed her. But after she has rested up, I need her help to feed them; they have pretty big appetites by then, You know!

"When they are six weeks old, the children break open the nest. We have a pretty anxious moment then because we believe in 'tough love'—Dr. Bird says it's the only way to fly—and so they take to the air immediately, without our help."

Raja's smile revealed a doting father. "They look pretty funny and awkward when they launch themselves into the air for the first time with their wings flapping and their feet flailing." He laughed with pride. "But it's all worth it." He reflected for a moment. "And that's how we have gained our world reputation for Parenting and House Building." He looked anxiously at the nest. For a moment he thought he had seen the tip of a beak.

NINE / IN WHICH *Moose conducts the second Tutorial, describing how Masters learn, keep growing, use the Seven Skills of the Trainer, develop their strengths while minimizing their weaknesses, learn patience and practice the philosophy of Kaizen. Tamias also learns the Laws of Solutions and Creativity.*

ah-rabar marched across the Boardwalk in his rather stiff style. Tamias decided to give him the "blur of fur." He stalked up behind him, and then, with a burst of acceleration, circled him with two laps. Bah-rabar pretended to ignore Tamias's high-strung squeaking and chirping. Tamias started to leap into the air every few feet, a sort of Chipmunk victory roll, as an alternative stress-relieving mechanism. He needed to decompress after the tensions of the day. And *what* a day! The vertigo had been forgotten. Even his unsettling meeting with Nemesis had been temporarily cast out of his mind. Tamias was pumped up by the excitement and quality of his classes.

"Don't You think You should conserve some of Your energy for Your meeting with Moose?" asked Bah-rabar, whose tone was intended to calm. But the over-excited Chipmunk stepped up his locomotion ratio with Bah-rabar to about twenty to one.

"How's it hangin' dude?" shouted Tamias, imitating Lenny the Gibbon as he completed another circuit.

"If You could match their skills as well as You mimic their dialect, You'd have it made in the shade!" said Bah-rabar, using the colloquialism self-consciously.

"Gimme a high five, dude!" The brown blur zipped across Bah-rabar.

As they seemed to be making rather slow progress, Bah-rabar decided to give Tamias some of his own medicine. "As the Mock Turtle sang to the Gryphon:

> *'Will You walk a little faster?' said a whiting to a snail,*
> *'There's a porpoise close behind us, and he's treading on my tail.'"*

"You're pretty gnarly, dude!" cried Tamias. Customer-People were parting in front of them like the Red Sea.

"*Kee-rah!*" Bah-rabar's bugle call was a device to contain Tamias as well as to signal their arrival to Moose and Kivali. Tamias slowed like a spinning top in its last few drunken turns.

"Have we finished impersonating the Greats?" smiled Bah-rabar, feigning a theatrical pose.

Tamias grinned. "One day, I'm going to show my cousin, Sciurus the Squirrel, how to do a *forward giant swing*, like Lenny's. And I'm going to ask Hoover to help me show Ondatra the Muskrat how to build a lodge to replace his hole-in-the-wall. And maybe I can learn nest building from Raja and Rani. Then I'd help Bill the Hairy Woodpecker to trade up his nest for a state-of-the-art nursery."

"Maybe You could show Moose how much You've learned today and see if You can complete the Masterclass first?" said Bah-rabar, trying to bring Tamias back to reality.

They had arrived at the Great Maple Tree. "Try to get a good night's sleep tonight, Tamias. You have been invited to attend a seminar tomorrow morning, chaired by Ulric the Arctic Wolf. He lives at the western end of the Zoo-Community. I'll meet You here first thing in the morning and we'll walk together to the Wood Bison Reserve on the banks of the Rouge River." Bah-rabar looked back at Tamias. "Take the Great Maple Tree to the ravine floor. Moose and Kivali are waiting. *Au revoir*, little friend, good luck with Your Tutorial."

Moose saw Tamias approaching. "Join Kivali and me at the pool," he shouted, beckoning with his great, padded paw.

"The sun still has much kindness left for us to enjoy today," Kivali added as Tamias arrived at the water's edge. "Please have a drink."

"Kivali and I have been enjoying this custom for a number of seasons," Moose said as Tamias arrived by the pool. "Every evening, as the sun kisses the horizon, we indulge in a few thoughtful moments together, discussing a point of principle. We call it our P.M. Poser. Today we have been discussing whether Masters are leaders or followers. What do You think?"

Tamias sat in reflection. "Interesting question! On balance, I think they are leaders. But, do You think they become temporary followers when they are learning?"

"You're probably right," Moose replied. "The Great Masters I have studied never seem to stop learning—either by learning from others or by constantly practicing, and, often, both." The three stared at the water pensively.

Moose broke the silence. "I trust Your day was rewarding?"

"Marvelous!" said Tamias. "One of the most exciting days I can remember. Thank You for choosing my tutors so well. They were superb!"

"You're welcome! But, Tamias, when You are learning, the teacher merely acts as the needle; the pupil is the thread. As Your mentor, I can help You by pointing You in the right direction. But like the needle from the thread, I must be separate from You in the end, because the strength, the fibre and the ability to bind everything together must be Yours."

Moose licked his paw and then stroked his left ear. He raised one eyebrow as if to confirm Tamias's understanding of his metaphor. Moose's comment reminded Tamias of his recent conversation with Nemesis. Was Moose sending him a signal?

Reassured by the contemplative expression on Tamias's face, Moose continued, "What was Raja and Rani's message for You?"

Tamias recalled his encounter with the Gray-cheeked Hornbills. "One of the strongest messages was that they work very hard and develop their strengths and minimize their weaknesses."

"Well said, Tamias! Let me share another example with You. My cousin, the Cheetah, is the fastest in the land. But he can maintain his speed for only a few hundred meters. He uses so much energy in trying to make a catch, that he must rest for at least thirty minutes before commencing another chase. Yet he fails in nine out of ten attempts."

Moose paused. "The Cheetah knows

**Moose's Law of Solutions: Complaining makes You part of the problem. Defining**

**successful outcomes makes You part of the solution.**

"Fortunately, his prey doesn't know his weakness. He stalks his quarry until he is very close to it, and by doing so exploits his skills of stealth, thus conserving energy. He never lets failure dim his belief that on every excursion, he will succeed. What other insights did Raja and Rani share with You?"

"The Hornbills' Mastery is based on a continuing and constant search for new knowledge," Tamias continued. "Their thirst for new and better techniques is insatiable. They're not complacent. They keep practicing and striving. Although they are Masters, they never seem to be too proud to learn, and the more they learn, the more they appreciate how much there is yet to learn."

Moose nodded. "Every experience in our world is a lesson. For instance, for most of us, the example of the parent is enormously important in training. Parents teach by demonstrating the same thing over and over again. That's how most of us impress ideas on our offspring. A Mink, for example, will put its offspring through many lessons in thoroughness, for adult Minks, like the rest of us, must learn to leave no stone unturned in the hunt for food. The objective is not the only point; it is the effort to improve ourselves that is just as valuable. And there is no end to this practice. What else did You find interesting?"

"Well, You mentioned practice. Both Brunel Beaver and Lenny Gibbon stressed this, too. In fact, at one point, the Great Gibbono lost his grip, nearly crashing to the forest floor. I was awed by the Gibbons' seeming disdain for failure, their constant search for new challenges, their faith and dependence on each other's skills and, above all, their modesty. I wondered though, if they should practice even more for such demanding tasks."

"But failure is part of practice!" Moose said, warming to the discussion. "I am sure that the Great Gibbono was grateful that he was shown a sign or warning signal to highlight the weak point in his practice. In mathematics, we call this getting rid of a minus by changing it into a plus. Inside or outside Yourself, You never have to change what You see, only the way You see it. And it is only when Your practice is greedy that You become discouraged with it.

"When You have practiced long and hard, You will learn not to expect rapid, frequent, extraordinary gains. Even though You try very hard, the progress You make is always little by little. And it's just as important to understand that it's not the honey that makes the tea sweet but the stirring."

The three exchanged glances of understanding and then Kivali spoke. "Tamias, my ancestors came from the islands of the Arctic, migrating south to India, China and Burma. One of them was a great philosopher who once taught:

> *If You wish to know the road to Mastery,*
> *Ask the one who has traveled it.*
> *Since the beginning of time, there were not two paths.*
> *Those who have arrived*
> *All walked the same road."*

"Let's continue for a moment with the theme that practice generates incremental progress," said Moose. "Are You familiar with the philosophy of *Kaizen?"*

Tamias shook his head.

"It's a philosophy which Nobunaga the Japanese Macaque helped me to introduce to the Zoo-Community, more than four seasons ago now, I suppose," said Moose, searching the sky for an imaginary calendar. "In his land, it's the single most important managerial concept. It is the stunningly simple philosophy of continuing, gradual improvement in one's personal and working life. Nobunaga helped me to make it one of the guiding philosophies of the Zoo-Community. You see, like any other organization, we have our problems—but we have succeeded in nourishing a culture that generates the freedom to identify and acknowledge these problems . . ."

"I agree that this is an elegant and appealing philosophy," said Tamias, "but what is the pay-off?"

"When using the word 'problem,'" Moose continued as if he had not been interrupted, "I mean anything that could inconvenience individuals downstream from You, whether it is a Manager-Person, a Customer-Person, a lover or friend or a colleague. And the most important point, You see, is that we should resolve *never* to pass a problem downstream. During Your Masterclass, Tamias, You will notice how we all strive in our own ways for excellence. We all have two parts to our tasks: the maintenance of standards and their improvement.

"In the Zoo-Community we spend more than fifty percent of our time on improvement—a focus of *constant revision and upgrading*—which emphasizes system and process innovation. We have so perfected *Kaizen* that many of us have graduated to the higher concept of *Warusa-kagen*, which is defined as 'recognizing things that are not yet problems but are not quite right.'"

"Isn't this just another way of describing innovation?" Tamias suggested.

"No, not really. Innovation is important, too, but it results in changing the status quo. *Kaizen*, on the other hand, results in the constant revision, upgrading and improvement of the status quo—progressing little by little, as I suggested before. It is true, however, that *Kaizen* and innovation share a common need: positive creativity. This is exemplified by

**Moose's Law of Creativity: Innovation results from building on new ideas, not criticizing them.**

This concept is as important to *Kaizen* as it is to innovation.

"The Gibbons have taught us to value the importance of practicing Your skill so frequently that You internalize it until it is 'forgotten.' And as You will have noticed, there is no particular way in true practice. They love what they do so much, that they get lost in it. In every relationship in life and at work the application of *Kaizen* and *Warusa-kagen* creates good bonding between us and the hearts and minds of others. It makes our lives *better*. This practice and dedication is the essence of Mastery. That is how You, like them, can become a true Master throughout Your work and Your life. Practicing a thousand times is discipline. Practicing ten thousand times is refining.

"All right!" said Moose, taking the Tutorial down a different path. "What did You learn from the Beavers?"

"Ummm. . . ." Tamias thought for a moment. "They showed me four key links in the chain of Mastery:

- Practice.
- Possessing and using the right tools.
- Understanding the larger concept of the task and the objectives.
- Keeping things as simple as possible.

"They made a series of complicated tasks and skills look very easy," reflected Tamias. "I think this is not just the result of practice alone, but also of training. I was struck by the obvious commitment and love that Brunel, as mentor, was investing in Hoover's training. They also seemed to have developed a concept of 'constructive decay' to effect change and improvement. For example, if their lodge should be weakened, they simply convert the problem into an opportunity to make it stronger. In this way they simply go with the flow."

Moose nodded his great square head in agreement. "Action should flow like the water around the rocks of a river. I like Your point about training. Let me share an important idea with You. Leadership is just another word for training. It is a fundamental part of everyone's job, no matter what their level or responsibility, and there are seven techniques that make it work:

- Criticize constructively and *never* criticize the new ideas of others; instead, build on them.
- Pay attention to complaints.
- Keep everyone informed and respect their right and need to know."
- Learn to be respected rather than liked.
- Ask Your subordinates for their advice and help.
- Develop a sense of responsibility in Your subordinates and expect the same thing from Your peers.
- Emphasize *Mastery* rather than *rules*.

Moose paused to slake his thirst, sucking up several gulps of water from the pond. He looked directly at the Chipmunk, then continued.

"Tamias, earlier You described what You called the four key links in the chain of Mastery, the second one being the importance of possessing and using the right tools. Let me give You some examples of the difference that having the right equipment can make. I know You were impressed with the acrobatic skills of the Gibbons, but consider this. My cousin, the Puma, can jump *up* seven meters from a standstill position, and *down*, from a tree for example, nineteen meters.

"Or, consider this. If a normal seventy-seven-kilo Customer-Person expended energy at the same rate as the Ruby-throated Hummingbird, it would have to eat, in a single day, one hundred and thirty kilos of hamburger, or twice its own weight in potatoes. The specially designed wings of the Swift allows it to fly nine hundred kilometers a day in search of insects at speeds of up to one hundred and seventy kilometers per hour. The wing design of the Peregrine Falcon allows them to dive at speeds of two hundred and eighty-two kilometers per hour.

"These animals demonstrate the standards of Mastery that can be achieved by exploiting the finest equipment available. But no amount of skill can compensate for inadequate equipment. Just as the Lark is the peerless musician and the Hummingbird is the Master Aerialist, neither would ever attempt to match the other's skills with their existing equipment."

Moose's torso shuddered as he stretched his paws in front of him, spreading his toes and displaying his powerful claws. His pads thumped to the ground again as he continued.

"Every member of our Community has a unique skill. Think of the Weaver Birds building their beautiful nests; the Pelicans fishing; the White-tailed Deer merging into the forest; the Varying Hares and Ptarmigans resembling leaves or snow, depending on the season. We all contribute a singular skill to the best of our ability. The result is balance, interdependence, synergy, mutualism. We make a beautiful noise. We are. We call it Nature."

Moose was getting restless. He stretched again, this time slowly raising his frame to the standing position. Tamias sensed that his Tutorial was drawing to a close. He was right.

"Tamias, You must get ready for an early start tomorrow. Let's tie a ribbon around the bouquet of ideas we have been discussing. The first of the Keys is called the Key of Mastery: "Undertaking whatever You do, in both Your personal and professional life, to the highest standards of which You are capable." The most critical thing to remember is that a great Master doesn't practice his craft for the material rewards, but if he's great, the rewards naturally follow. As you remember, this is

**Moose's Law of Mastery: Mastery never seeks reward; rewards always find Mastery."**

Kivali rose to her feet now, too. "I have watched You during this Tutorial, Tamias. You have done well during the first part of Your Masterclass. Remember to keep Your mind open, to challenge Your tutors. Do not be biased—too much is as bad as too little. When You say something to someone, do not fence with them intellectually. Listen to the objections others make until they find their own weaknesses."

Tamias reflected on this last piece of advice. If Kivali and Moose had been aware of his conversation with Nemesis, they might have appreciated its additional pertinence. After thanking them both for their hospitality, Tamias bade them good night and ascended the Great Maple Tree.

During the walk home, he wondered if genius was simply the highest order of Mastery—or was it, like innovation, simply nothing more than the act of perceiving the ordinary in an unconventional way?

# The
# Second
# Key

# *Chemistry*

Relating so well with others on a personal and social level that they actively
seek to associate themselves with
You.

TEN / IN WHICH *Tamias recalls the concept of "beginners' mind" and Tamias and Bah-rabar attend a Conference of Arctic Wolves, during which they learn how Chemistry is achieved through good communications, bonding, management of conflict, "space" and camaraderie.*

t was a glorious morning. Tamias and Bah-rabar arrived at the Wood Bison Reserve at the same time. Tamias had taken the Grizzly Bear Trail, chirping cheery greetings to the Lynx, the Bobcat and the Cougars on the way. It was a long walk for Bah-rabar, but he showed no signs of exertion. The Chipmunk's mood matched the good weather. He decided to ask Bah-rabar a question he had been saving for just the right moment. This was it.

Tamias cleared his throat. "If I . . ." He stopped to correct himself. "*When* I successfully complete my Masterclass, what do You think my responsibilities in the Zoo-Community will be?" He was aware of the agenda hidden within the question.

Bah-rabar looked at him like Peacocks do and replied, "The literal answer to Your question is that You will join a group of experts who maintain and improve the process of generating new life from decay. I believe that searching for fallen beechnuts and acorns among the woodlands is an important part of this process. But if You think about Your work in such a prosaic way, You will fail to appreciate the real point and purpose of Your future with the Zoo-Community.

"As You know, the two principal assets to qualify for consideration as a member of our organization are a well-seeing attitude and good mental equipment—attitude and intelligence. But after You have joined, You will not be required to be this or that, but simply *to be, to the best of Your ability*. It is the Tao of the Zoo-Community. This is what the Three Keys are for."

This advice gave Tamias quite a different perspective on his future career. He spotted a sunflower seed in the grass. As he cracked it open, he realized that he was beginning to understand more clearly the potential of the Three Keys.

Tamias stared vacantly into the rolling bush country. In the middle distance he saw the Arctic Wolves. He had learned about "The Big Bad Wolves" when he was young, and most of what he knew, he didn't like. Even the thought of today's Chemistry class with them made him nervous.

"Why are the Wolves so important as examples of Chemistry, Bah-rabar? Back home, we are taught to stay away from them; they can be mean critters."

"It's funny that You should say that, Tamias," responded Bah-rabar. "Nearly all rodents of Your dimensions are taught to feel the same way. For most of us, it has been a source of fascination and concern that the Wolves suffer from such bad press. It is ironic that they have honed internal communications among pack members so well while paying so little attention to their external communications. In fact, the Wolves themselves are so concerned, their conference today is on this very issue. When they heard You would be here, they extended You an invitation."

Tamias turned to look at the Wolves again. He tried to use Moose's advice as a kind of intellectual prism:

*If Your mind is empty, it is always ready for a new idea, a different perspective; it is open to everything. In the beginner's mind there are many possibilities; in the expert's mind there are few.*

Tamias decided that on this subject, at least, he must be an expert!

His nervousness was not lessened by the eerie howl that rose from the valley floor. It was a long, deep, mournful call, very familiar to Tamias. The pack members were communicating to each other over long distances in the form of a reveille. The single howl became a chorus produced by several Wolves, a powerful, early-morning tension releaser—for the Wolves, anyway!

"When one Wolf howls, others can hardly resist joining in," Bah-rabar commented. "See how they all begin howling immediately? Even Customer-People who can make a passable imitation of their howl frequently elicit a response. Wolves understand the need for good communications. They also appreciate that even team players need 'space'—Wolf packs are composed of individuals who respect each other's individuality. Therefore pack members are often dispersed. For an animal that hunts socially, it is important to have an effective means of remaining in contact. Quite musical, isn't it?"

Tamias never failed to be impressed by Bah-rabar's erudition, but he wasn't sure if "musical" was the word he would have chosen. "Unsettling" or "eerie," maybe, but not "musical"!

A single file of about a dozen Wolves wended its way towards a large granite boulder. "Looks like they're getting ready to start," Bah-rabar said. "Let's go over and join them."

This statement surprised Tamias.

Bah-rabar noticed Tamias's puzzled expression. "I'm very interested in this subject, and I've been invited to attend, too," he said.

Ulric was the dominant male of the pack, the Alpha male. He had already taken up his Leader's position beside the Assembly Rock. Tamias and Bah-rabar hurried down the river bank until they came to the fringe of the undergrowth. They looked for a comfortable, unobtrusive spot, settling for a patch of field mustard at the base of a tall Poplar.

The Arctic Wolves had formed a large semicircle around the Assembly Rock. Ulric was counting heads prior to starting the proceedings. He had a creamy-white back, flanks and tail, but his belly and throat were even brighter, offering a sharp contrast with his moist black nose and sable lips. At fifty-five kilos, he didn't have to say "Sir" to anyone. He scanned the pack with the golden punctuation points of his eyes. He called the meeting to order as he mounted the Assembly Rock.

"Distinguished guests and fellow members of the *Canis lupus* family," he began, "it is an honor for me to welcome You to this conference on the image of our species. Apart from the honorable members of our pack, we also have some esteemed visitors, and I would like to introduce them to You. On my immediate left is Mephitis the Skunk; next to him, Mustela the Mink and Rocky the Raccoon. At the foot of the Poplar we have Bah-rabar, our eminent Masterclass Guide, and Tamias, a prospective member of the

Zoo-Community to whom we extend a special welcome.''

Ulric continued introducing conference guests, first those on the ground, then those in the trees, until he had familiarized the gathering with all of the attendees.

"Let me explain today's agenda to You. First I will sketch a brief history of our species, and then I hope to give You a picture of the problem we are facing. Following this, I will throw it open to the floor for an informal brainstorming session. Is that all right with everyone?''

Ulric scanned the pack members, then the forest edge and finally the trees. Sensing no disagreement, he continued.

"We are the largest *Canid*,'' Ulric said, "our roots being in North America. Today, our family numbers about twenty-five thousand in Canada and Alaska. But in Europe, we have been the victims of massive destruction and have been virtually wiped out. We are attempting to reestablish ourselves in parts of Spain, Italy, Germany and Eastern Europe, and we have been very successful in doing so in the USSR, especially in Siberia, where large populations now live.''

Ulric stopped to make sure that everyone could hear him adequately. Raising the pitch of his voice by a tone, he went on: "The history of our poor public image and the persecution that has resulted is long and sad. Some of the myths originated, perhaps, with the legend of Romulus and Remus, the founders of Rome who were, supposedly, suckled by a Wolf. One of the biblical authors wrote in Matthew 7:15, 'Beware of false prophets which come to You in sheep's clothing, but inwardly are ravening Wolves.' You may have heard of the mythical Teutonic Wolf that devoured the sun at the end of the world! And most of You will be familiar with *Aesop's Fables, Little Red Riding Hood, The Three Little Pigs, Peter and the Wolf* and a more recent travesty, Jack London's *Call of the Wild.*"

The lone caw of a Crow broke the silent tension in Ulric's audience.

"For European farmers living in serfdom," he continued, "we became the embodiment of terror, since they believed that Wolves in the cattle stall could result in economic ruin for their landowners, who, as a result, might then not be able to afford their tithe or provide winter supplies for salting. After the Thirty Years War, our numbers multiplied again, but this prevented new settlements. Landowners reacted by ordering our mass destruction. We were driven into nets and slaughtered. Improved weaponry and the introduction of strychnine in the eighteenth century led to more systematic attacks.

"By the beginning of the Napoleonic wars, we had

lost the fight, having been eliminated from many parts of Europe. At the turn of the eighteenth century, each Wolf kill was recorded in the hunting annual. Kills were often commemorated by the laying of Wolf stones.''

Ulric paused to catch his breath. ''Two hundred years ago, Wolves were routinely tried and burned at the stake.''

There were gasps of horror from many. Ulric was big, but he had a heart to match. The emotion showing in his face was reflected in many others'. He breathed deeply and braced himself to continue.

''More than eighty thousand of us were poisoned, shot or dynamited in our dens between 1883 and 1919 in the state of Montana alone. Subsequently, the State Veterinarian was ordered to inoculate all trapped Wolves with sarcoptic mange and release them so that they would infect the remainder of our packs. Even though we are an endangered species today, many American farmers use the 'three S' method to continue the carnage: 'Shoot, shovel and shut-up.'''

As Ulric wound up his summary, the tremble in his voice betrayed his deep passion.

The crowd was hushed. No one spoke for nearly a minute.

It was Erith the Porcupine who broke the silence. He had settled into a fork in the Poplar Tree above

Tamias and Bah-rabar. His quiet voice, punctuated by soft snorts and grunts, cut across the silent summer air, reaching every ear.

"The problem is that perception is reality and reality is perception!" he said. "Some of Your behavior is frightening to Customer-People and they have exaggerated this behavior over time. The exaggerations have become the reality. You have failed to capitalize on Your attributes. If You did, *they* might become exaggerated, generating positive exaggerations, and these would, in turn, become the new reality." *Grunt, snort, bark.*

"I agree," Dolly the Bobolink trilled. "The irony is that the social organization of Wolves, in some ways, resembles that of Customer-People. Even they must know that it is one of the most highly developed in the animal kingdom. Your division of labor and Your communication and organization achievements are the envy of our land. I've often admired the extended family that forms the well-defined hierarchy within Your packs. And I especially like the way You maintain Your social hierarchy through specific ritualized postures and behavior patterns in order to preserve the pack as a social unit. Erith is right, You ought to promote these traits and skills."

Selina, the Alpha female of the pack, spoke next. "For those of You who are not familiar with our culture, perhaps I should fill in some background. As

You all know, our social behavior arose chiefly because of the nature of our feeding habits. We are big-game hunters. It would be difficult for a single Wolf to kill a big animal, so natural selection has acted to produce our social hunting and group life.

"Young members of the family learn how to capture their prey by accompanying and watching the Master Hunters in our pack. Before they are grown, they may help in running down a Caribou, but we do not allow them to touch it until an older and more experienced pack member makes the kill. Eventually, they are allowed to stalk, attack, kill and eat the prey. In this way they learn Mastery.

"This learning process never stops, for every hunt is different, possessing new challenges. Our techniques are so successful that sometimes an adaptable member of the Dog or Weasel family may join the pack, learning to travel and hunt our way! We have found that there is no shortage of individuals with a strong drive to succeed who wish to join our successful teams. We have learned never to maintain members in our packs who are not a natural fit and, conversely, to welcome anyone who brings good Chemistry and is willing to contribute to our teamwork."

"Good point!" observed Ulric, adding, "We have found that among existing and potential pack members, *excellence searches for excellence*. Quality players seek to ally themselves with other quality players. Masters are attracted to other Masters. Through this commitment to team excellence, we develop total faith in our pack colleagues, form ourselves into effective teams and forge a powerful team spirit.

"As Selina has said, our prey animal's weight may be as much as ten times our own, and so we must hunt as a pack. The pack size is limited by our ability to feed ourselves. We do not attack every animal that we come into contact with. We test an animal first, nearly always taking only the old, the weak or the sick. This is our contribution to the ecosystem. We assist in the maintenance of healthy stock among prey animals."

"Then why don't You say so?" squeaked Erith. "You should look at our example; it is only because of our concerted publicity campaign that we have recently been able to dispel the notion that we Porcupines shoot our quills at our enemies.

"I've heard, for example, that on Isle Royale, the Moose killed most often by Wolves are those less than one season old and older than eight years. There are between twenty and thirty Wolves on the island and nine hundred to a thousand Moose, and this relationship has been stable over many years. That doesn't match Your poor image at all. Why don't You publicize it?" *Grunt, snort, bark.*

A number of the Wolves barked their applause for Erith's positive contribution.

Bar-rabar stepped forward. "I'm a rather independent individual, but I've long been an admirer of Your commitment to teamwork. You develop tremendous unity of purpose. You understand the power of synergy. I know You believe that teamwork is a higher order of activity than internal competition. From You I have learned that successful teams only compete with other teams. Many could profit from this philosophy. Why don't You promote it?"

Bah-rabar retired into the field mustard again and Tamias bathed in the reflected glory of his friend's presentation.

Marmot the Woodchuck rose on his hind feet so that he could see the others better (and perhaps to afford himself a modicum of stature).

"I'm pretty much of a loner, too," he said, "and I recognize that it's always easier to talk about the problems of others than Your own, but You are holding a very successful conference here today. Like most successful teams, You have created and cultivated networks of friends and influence.

"You have not developed Chemistry with Your internal teams alone, but You have also recognized the equal importance of bonding with all of the others with whom You share Your environment, compete with and depend on. I think You should be congratulated for realizing that You must have the vision to build networks beyond Your own immediate kin."

"I have listened with great interest to Your many contributions," Ulric said. "A central theme running through most of Your comments is that we should try to alter the public's perception of Wolves by promoting our strengths. I find it interesting to note how You see us in ways that we can not. We are indebted to You for Your solid contributions. May I suggest that You might welcome a short break? I would be grateful if we could all reconvene when, say, the sun is directly over the Basswood Tree?"

Several of the conference participants dispersed into the bush. Many broke into conversation. Others just stretched and fooled around.

Several Wolves ranged across their territory, exploiting their highly developed sense of smell through a procedure of marking, which they accomplished by raising the leg and urinating.

Bah-rabar turned to Tamias, remarking, "Urine marking is done by all Wolves to mark territories, paths and hunting zones. Because it is repeatedly carried out at the same spot, it helps Wolves become acquainted with other members as well as enabling them to become familiar with a surrounding area. You may notice, too, that subordinate males seldom risk raised-leg-marking in the presence of Ulric. This is a ceremonial right that belongs to the Alpha male alone."

Tamias couldn't avoid the need to scratch his ear any longer. Bah-rabar waited patiently. The task efficiently undertaken with his hind foot, Tamias once again gave Bah-rabar his undivided attention.

"And as I mentioned in the conference," Bah-rabar continued, "the competitive energies of Wolves are mostly directed towards outsiders. This makes Wolves more effective teams than many other animals, where there is frequently as much competition within teams as between them. I've heard that this is especially true of Customer-people. This, of course, in any grouping, tends to be counterproductive."

As some of the Wolves returned from their break, one made the mistake of crossing another's territory, provoking a scuffle. The two squared off, circling each other closely. Tamias smelled trouble.

Salivating, powerful teeth were bared. The Wolves' ears were pricked up, foreheads wrinkled and tails erect. One Wolf lunged at the other, its jaws snapping shut loudly. With the footwork of a water strider, the other sidestepped, presenting a void to the first Wolf. After several successful parries, the smaller of the two was brought to its haunches, the bigger one hunching over it in victory. The subordinate Wolf rolled over, lying half on its back and half on its side in a gesture of submission and defeat.

Tension was in the air—Tamias held his breath. But this display secured the release of the vanquished, for Wolves seldom attack each other in earnest. The larger Wolf eased back a few steps, permitting the loser to roll over and slink away with his tail tucked between his legs to join his friends who had begun to reform the semicircle. With the flourish of a swash-buckler, the dominant Wolf marked the scene of battle with his scent.

The conference participants erupted spontane-ously into lively chatter, debating among themselves the relative merits of the duelists and their finer points of style.

Ulric reached the Assembly Rock with a few loping strides and then brought the meeting to order again. As the participants settled down, Lepus the Snow-shoe Hare thumped the ground to gain Ulric's atten-tion.

"We have just seen an example of what Erith and Dolly were suggesting before our break," Lepus said. "As many of us have always known, Wolves look like they are fighting when they are playing. It looks pretty scary to most of us, all that growling, gnashing of teeth and flying fur, but we know that the law of the pack dictates that no member should kill another. Often, the worst fate for a loser is banish-ment, these losers leaving the pack to travel as lone Wolves.

"You demonstrate that wonderful 'sense of family' that is the hallmark of all effective teams and Your avoidance of real conflict underscores Your successful teamwork. You've done a wonderful job of developing superb communications within Your own ranks, but Your inattention to external communications has resulted in the bum-rap image from which You now suffer. I think Your public image could be improved if You considered mounting a traveling roadshow featuring duels between some of Your fittest members in which they would help to erase the notion of 'The Big Bad Wolf.'"

The discussion after the break was superb. Many speakers made brilliant points during the balance of the morning. Parus the Chickadee recited a poem he had set to music praising the Wolves for their excellent communication. Hyla the Gray Treefrog provided a remarkable account of the similarities between the hierarchy of the Wolf pack and that of the Frog pond. Chelydra the Snapping Turtle offered a humorous comparison between the unwarranted poor image of Snapping Turtles and Wolves, and asked for a copy of the conference proceedings. Agelaius the Red-winged Blackbird complimented the Wolves on their love of groups and extolled the potential of organizations, citing the annual migration of tens of millions of his members from Canada to the southern United States.

Just before the attendees adjourned for lunch, Bah-rabar suggested to Tamias that they should sneak away, so that Tamias could attend his afternoon class with the Meerkats.

After exchanging farewells with their immediate neighbors, they started the long trek to the Africa Pavilion.

ELEVEN / IN WHICH *Tamias meets Nemesis again, learns how deceiving appearances can be and remembers that fear of change leads to decay and death.*

Tamias
was so en-
grossed
with the
arguments
presented
at the
Wolves'
conference
that he
feared he
had not
allowed
enough
time to
get to his
next ren-
dezvous, so
he went on
ahead of
Bah-
rabar.
He was
surprised,
therefore,
to find his
splendidly
plumed friend
waiting for him
outside the main
entrance of
the Africa
Pavilion.
Tamias
imagined
that Bah-
rabar must

have taken another of his many short cuts, but before this riddle could be solved, the Peacock proffered an unusually effusive greeting.

"I trust that your class with the Meerkats will be both instructive and amusing, Tamias," he said.

The Chipmunk blinked, peering into the Peacock's inscrutable face. His sense of confusion changed to unease.

The Peacock continued, "To learn about the pain of power, you must speak to Moose. But to learn about the pleasure of power, you must speak to Nemesis. You are destined for great things in the Zoo-Community, Tamias. Choose your mentors carefully and learn well from your classes. *Nemesis* will show you the Three Keys!"

A crowd of Customer-People ran noisily between them, bisecting their conversation. Tamias started to reply as soon as they passed, but he stopped; Bah-rabar had disappeared.

The sun-baked pavement hurt Tamias's feet as he skimmed across it, searching the forest of legs for Bah-rabar. There was no sign of him. He beat a frenzied path through the Customer-People to the Elephant Pavilion, where Tequila was enjoying her siesta in the midday sun.

"Have You seen my friend Bah-rabar?" he wanted to know. But the grand old dame of the African Ele-phants slowly shook her head from side to side as she sprayed herself with a cooling plume of dust.

Tamias could not afford to keep the Meerkats waiting any longer. The Gray-cheeked Hornbills shouted a cheery welcome as he entered the Africa Pavilion. He squeaked a friendly response and hurried down the stairs. As he jumped off the last step, an elevator disgorged its cargo of Customer-People.

He scratched his chin, waiting for a moment near the African Lungfish. Then another familiar voice prevailed upon his ears.

"Ahh! Tamias-s-s! How nice to s-s-see you again!" The unctuous tones dripped from the unsmiling face of the Royal Python. Though Tamias was late, hidden fetters restrained his advance.

"How are You today, er, Nem?" asked Tamias politely.

"Just fine, Tam, just fine," replied the Serpent. "I won't keep you as I know you're in a rush, but tell me, have you thought any more about our little conversation yesterday?"

"Well, to be quite honest, my schedule has been a bit crowded and..."

"No problem, no problem," whispered Nemesis. "I am s-s-sure that you have been noticing those inefficiencies that I mentioned. You know, just the other day I was recollecting that a few years ago, the Zoo-Community was organized by s-s-species. In those days I lived in the S-s-snake House with all my friends. The Orang-utans, Gorillas and Mandrills all lived together in the Ape House with their friends, too. It had been that way at the Zoo-Community for eighty-s-s-six years. Then s-s-some wise guy Manager Person decided to reorganize us all into five Zoogeographic regions: Africa, Australasia, Indo-Malaya, the Americas and Eurasia.

"Before then, the Lions, Tigers, Leopards and Cheetahs had all been one happy family in the Cat House. That's when Moose and Kivali were given their own pad. Went to their heads, you know. Moose has grown pompous. That's why it's time for new leadership and a different vision of the Zoo-Community. If you will help me, I will s-s-share that new vision and my power with you."

"I can sympathize with what You are saying," said Tamias, considering the merits of Nemesis's persuasive argument, "but isn't it true that the only alternative to change and improvement is stagnation? Don't we need to adapt to new ways of thinking and methods of doing things?"

Nemesis's eyes bored into Tamias. "Change for the s-s-sake of change, Tamias-s-s, is the philosophy of the cancer cell!" He spat the words in contempt. "When I assume my rightful position in the Zoo-Community, I'll put an end to all this pointless change." He unlinked one of his coils, draping it languorously over a damp tree stump.

"Kaizen, change and innovation have undermined the values that made this a great institution," the Serpent continued, hypnotizing Tamias with his black, beady eyes.

"One of the first Zoo-Communities in the world was established one hundred and s-s-sixty years ago in London, England. The Manager-People were scientists: zoologists, botanists and biologists. Their focus was on the preservation and welfare of the members of the Zoo-Community. This pattern remained unchanged as the tall oaks added one hundred and fifty rings to their girth. Then, Kaizen, change and innovation replaced predictability and certainty. The scientists were replaced by MBAs, corporate executives, fund-raisers and high-profile directors. The new focus became human resource management, revenue generation, tourism and marketing."

Nemesis bobbed his head while fixing his unblinking gaze on Tamias. "You know, Tamias-s-s, together we can make this a better place. Can I count on you?"

Tamias thought that Nemesis had overlooked the Zoo-Community's commitment to preservation, conservation, education and research, but he didn't want to prolong their discussion.

"Er, Nem, You offer a very interesting argument. May I think about it over the next day and a half?"

"No problem! No problem! But remember, if you

give me your help, I'll give you my word—we'll s-s-share the power!''

TWELVE / IN WHICH *Tamias meets Suri the Meerkat, who demonstrates the fun, positive attitude, social interaction and integration of ego that characterize potent teams, and the way each member assumes leadership responsibilities.*

uri was standing upright on her hind legs, supporting herself with her stiffened tail. From her vantage point on top of the limestone outcrop, she held forth to an admiring audience.

"One day, a small Ground Snake was hiding in its hole when a Meerkat approached. *'Grunt, Squeak, Hiss,'* he heard the Meerkat say. Then the sound of a furious Hyena— *'Woof...Woof...Woof...'*—a spitting retreat, and then merciful silence. The Snake crept out of his hole and the Meerkat pounced on him, remarking as he ate him up, 'I always knew it would be useful to have a second language!'"

Shrieks of delight erupted from the other Meerkats. Some fell about the ground, doubled up in hysteria, while others leaned against each other, unable to control themselves. Suri, sensing that she was on a roll, pressed the advantage of the gifted raconteuse.

"How do Elephants make love under water?" she asked. The requisite straight man volunteered, "I don't know, Suri. How do Elephants make love under water?"

"They first remove their trunks," came Suri's punch line. More waves of hilarity.

Tamias could hear the swells of Meerkat laughter before he could see their source. He noticed as he passed the Bongos that these beautiful African forest antelopes, too, were much amused by the vaudevillian wit of their neighbors.

Suri spotted Tamias climbing the cedar posts that served as their territorial boundary. She watched the Chipmunk scale the fencing for a moment and then issued a sharp bark to her troops. The effect was immediate: every last Meerkat froze in sudden, rigid silence.

It reminded Tamias of the game of "statues" he had enjoyed so much with his brothers and sisters many seasons ago. But now he had been presented with the backs of a dozen little furry soldiers, with coats of long, soft, grizzled-gray fur blending into black, transverse bars. Their heads were almost white, with small black ears, and their yellowish tails were as long as their bodies. When these funsters were made, their Maker must have dipped the ends of their tails in coal tar.

Suri gave a hoot, startling Tamias and causing every Meerkat to wheel around suddenly and face him. They all peered somberly at Tamias with big, black, baleful eyes, shrouded with what seemed to be an unfashionable excess of eyeliner and mascara. Here were the original Schmoos.

Suddenly they broke the conspiracy of silence, erupting into loud chuckles and gurgles and scampering about the rocks and sand shouting frenzied "tee-hees." Tamias was annoyed; he felt uncomfortable and embarrassed.

Suri broke away from the silliness and as she approached, Tamias let loose with a piece of his mind. "Suri, I came here today to learn. I've had to rush to be punctual and I'd be most grateful if we could get down to business!"

"Whoa, Tamias!" said Suri. "Lighten up. This *is* the lesson!"

"What do You mean?" said Tamias, nonplussed.

"What You *think* You heard was a group of Meerkats being foolish. But what You might have heard—especially if You had listened instead of thinking about what You were going to do or say next—was a very closely knit team, carefully demonstrating to You the importance of fun and social interaction in building Chemistry."

Tamias was contrite, but Suri put him at ease.
"Don't feel badly. You're here to learn and every experience is part of that learning. Your reaction is typical. But before we go any further, Tamias, perhaps I should explain how important *listening* is for us Meerkats. Have You noticed how we take turns in sentry duty on top of the rocks? That's because we're small and vulnerable. We must always remain alert to danger. We all take turns, scanning for Eagles, Wildcats and Foxes. We stand upright, so that we can throw all our physical energy into listening. We don't just listen with our ears. Body language is important, too."

Wrinkling her damp dark nose and wiggling her small black ears, Suri moved so close to Tamias that only a whisker separated their faces. "The eyes and nose can hear, too!" she breathed into Tamias's face. Then she jumped back and pointed to all her friends. "Look at them. If they didn't have exceptional listening skills, how would they establish good relationships? How would they become good negotiators? How would they set and achieve goals or assess performance?" Using her tail as a prop, Suri balanced perfectly upright on her hind legs, surveying the territory and checking out her team before continuing.

"We Meerkats enjoy the close contact we have with each other. We play-fight together throughout the day and we even sleep stacked up in heaps on one another. We spend a lot of time grooming each other's fur, combing, nibbling and licking.

"Stroking, investing, teaching—these are means by which Chemistry is enhanced and mutual profit generated. Sometimes a baby-sitter will be a recently joined member who is earning the trust of his or her colleagues. Members of successful teams understand that enlightened self-interest is a gift to the team—You are most useful to Yourself when You are useful to others."

Tamias spoke up. "It sounds like an adaptation of

**Moose's Law of Enlightened Self-Interest: In order to receive from Your employer, You must first give to Your Customer."**

"It is, really," agreed Suri. "We share equally: all the food, all the child-rearing and baby-sitting, all the chores, all the sentry duties, all the fighting and all the fun! In our sparse and dangerous surroundings, our survival depends upon our mutualism, our cooperation, just like our good friends, the Wolves."

Suri paused. A mite disappeared down a small hole in the dust. Suri's two front paws became an excavating machine as she sank into the ground. The mite became a snack.

Savoring the morsel, she continued, "For instance, when a sentry spots a predator, instead of running away, we come together in a close grouping and charge the enemy. We try to give the appearance of a large animal in constant motion and the leading member of the group rises on her hind legs, pretending to be the head of the 'animal.' With enough hissing and growling, we'll usually confuse the enemy so much that they flee. This degree of coordination can only be achieved by teams with very finely tuned listening and communication skills.''

"You seem to stress teamwork," said Tamias. "But apart from Yourself, there doesn't appear to be a hierarchy, such as that possessed by the Wolves."

"Very perceptive observation! We work differently from the Wolves. Like them, we build our relationships on bonding, friendship and empathy. But we have no room in our culture for teams that are dominated by any single ego. Even in my case, I see myself more as a catalyst and coordinator than leader. Or perhaps I should turn that idea around: Every one of our members is a leader. Moose will explain this concept to You when he reviews his Law of Leadership."

The Meerkats broke up from their huddles and wandered off in different directions, chattering and twittering to themselves.

"What are all Your friends doing now?" Tamias asked.

"They are practicing their self-talk."

"Is that like reinforcing one's positive mental attitude?"

"In a way, yes. Although we all live under the same sky, we don't all share the same horizon all of the time. We encourage each member of the Meerkat team to play a part in reinforcing the self-esteem of the group, so that we *can* share the same horizon. With such a busy agenda, and so many priorities and goals, some members may get down on themselves. But we can't afford any drags. If every team member contributes, in even the smallest way, to the others' zest for life, the whole team wins.

"We have no room for whiners and dumpers. We want everyone on our team to *laugh with their tails*. Dangers, disappointments and defeats have to be overcome, walked away from, detoured, forgotten or accepted, but never complained about. Successful teams never communicate with negatives. So, from time to time, all Meerkat team members go off for a few moments on their own and rehearse their self-talk, retuning their perspective so that it remains upbeat.

"For example," Suri went on, "When You arrived You said to Yourself, 'I'm angry!', and You and I nearly got off on the wrong foot. But if Your self-talk had been tuned, You might have said, 'I want to be angry because I normally get my way and these Meerkats aren't letting me, but instead I'm going to see what I can learn by watching them.' See how it works?"

"Absolutely! And I'm very sorry that I misunderstood You." Tamias stared at the ground thoughtfully for a moment or two, looking very much like a Chipmunk about to articulate a concept that would forever change the universe. He raised his head as if it took great effort, looked Suri directly in the eye and said, "By the way, did You know that the Brahmin bulls can still be found wandering up and down the steps of a famous bank in Calcutta?" Tamias paused. "They are said to be the biggest depositors!"

Suri laughed with her tail.

Tamias winked at her as they shared the joke together and said, "Thanks for a very good class!"

THIRTEEN / IN WHICH *Moose conducts the third Tutorial, and Tamias learns the Three Level Theory of Communication. He also learns how Chemistry is based on leadership, good listening skills, avoidance of negative criticism and the sharing of power, authority and credit.*

amias had become expert at zigzagging between the legs of Customer-People. Unwittingly they opened the doors leading out of the Africa Pavilion for him. Once outside, he saw Bah-rabar sauntering in the late afternoon sun. He was pleased to see his friend waiting for him. He had been eager to talk to him ever since they had become parted in the crowd earlier that day.

"Bah-rabar, just before my meeting with the Meerkats, You said to me, 'To learn about the pain of power, You must speak to Moose. But to learn about the pleasure of power, You must speak to Nemesis.' What exactly did You mean?"

Bah-rabar didn't answer immediately. Tamias followed him as he walked down the Lion Trail, towards the Indo-Malaya Pavilion. Small clusters of Customer-People and their young stopped to admire and chatter at the pair. Bah-rabar and Tamias rewarded them by hamming it up. Tamias sat on his haunches, feverishly rubbing his nose and washing his ears with his forepaws. Bah-rabar provided an iridescent display of *haute couture* by fanning his tail.

As the crowd passed, Bah-rabar turned to Tamias. Choosing his words carefully, he said, "The Serpent has many faces, and though he lives in every part of our lives, he speaks with one tongue; one voice with many forms. In the same way, it was not I who spoke with You, but one of Nemesis's retinue, Rakshasa."

"Why did Rakshasa trick me into believing that he was You?" Tamias asked irritably.

"This is for You to discover. I do not wish to discuss this further with You just now."

They crossed the Boardwalk together, Tamias walking along the handrail while Bah-rabar strode across the cedar planks. Although this enabled them to converse at the same level, they were silent. Tamias was puzzled. It was odd for Bah-rabar to be so unhelpful. Hidden within the Peacock's inscrutable response was a message he would have to work out on his own.

They approached the home of Moose and Kivali. Bah-rabar broke the silence. "Tomorrow is the last and most important day of Your Masterclass. In the morning, I'll meet You at the Hippopotamus pool and we'll walk from there to the Cape Fur Seals. Along the way, I'll introduce You to some of my friends from the African Savannah.

"Last night I suggested that You treat Yourself to a good night's sleep; that advice is even more relevant tonight. Also, I recommend only limited studying; if You don't know it now, You never will, and sleep will yield more sagacity than study.

"Finally, eat a hearty breakfast in the morning. You will need Your wits about You during Moose's final Tutorial and I subscribe to the notion that if You treat Your body right, Your mind will benefit."

With that physiological homily, Bah-rabar strode into the evening to join his friends at the Village Edge. Bah-rabar's words trailed behind him: "I hope that Your Tutorial with Moose this evening is very rewarding."

Tamias sprang up into the lower branches of the Great Maple Tree, settling into a comfortable fork for a moment of reflection. Does Nemesis have a hidden agenda? Why wasn't Bah-rabar more forthcoming about the Serpent? What was the riddle he was trying to solve? Why was the Masterclass such a trial?

A honey-dipped voice insinuated itself into his thoughts. It was Kivali. "You're early!" she purred from below. "We have some time before our P.M.

Poser. Come on down."

Tamias's growing familiarity with Kivali had not lessened her charisma. Kivali's eyes shone like two citrine gems set in virgin snow. Her moist pink nose was dappled with hazel patterns and framed by a white velvet muzzle. Long white whiskers sprang like gossamer quills, from rows of flecked sienna. Tamias had tried to describe her to his family last night, but the necessary poetry had eluded him.

"Moose is still sleeping," Kivali said gently as the Chipmunk slipped down the tree.

Perhaps an opportunity had presented itself, Tamias thought to himself. "That's rather fortunate, Kivali, because I'd very much like to pick Your brains about something. Would You mind?"

"Not at all," Kivali's tone was sympathetic. "Let's sit by the pool. What's troubling You?"

Tamias sipped water at the pool's edge and then turned to Kivali. He respected her warmth and wisdom. After a moment, he took a breath and proceeded. "Is Nemesis a credible threat to Moose's status as Zoo-Guru?"

Kivali masked her surprise. The question was bound to arise eventually, but Masterclass novitiates seldom appreciated the insidious threat posed by Nemesis until later in the curriculum.

Kivali's smile was more helpful than her response. "That's a question that only You can answer,

Tamias.''

More riddles, Tamias thought to himself. He was disappointed. He had hoped that Kivali would help him unlock this enigma. He searched her face for inspiration, but it gave up no secrets.

He considered the question further, concentrating his thoughts. He recalled Bah-rabar's earlier remarks: ''The Serpent has many faces, and though he lives in every part of our lives, he speaks with one tongue; one voice with many forms...''

Slowly, tentative explanations began to form in his mind. Ideas tumbled from his mouth as he blurted out his loosely formed thoughts: ''I think I have it! I think I have it! Nemesis epitomizes how the Zoo-Community pivots between the forces of change and those of tradition, between the dynamic and the static, between adaptation and resistance. It's a sort of axis between emphasis on process rather than result, between doing things right instead of doing the right thing.'' He looked at Kivali for a signal that he was on track.

''Go on!'' It was Moose's voice that now encouraged Tamias. Lying in the grass a short distance away, the Head Cat had been wafting in and out of sleep. Now he was listening to Tamias, one eye open.

''It is a contest between competing attitudes,'' Tamias said. ''There are many like Nemesis in the Zoo-Community, in a family and in any organization.

They purvey superficially plausible and seductive arguments that promote reactionary thinking. I guess rejecting the temptation to revert to the comfortable, well-trodden path is the difficult but necessary duty of every individual."

Moose was lying on his side. He extended his limbs to their limits and then arched his back, stretching every sinew until it vibrated. He rolled onto his stomach as a luxuriant yawn overtook him.

Tamias was temporarily side-tracked by this private moment. He re-ran his assumptions in his mind's eye, detecting as he did so a gap in his reasoning.

"How do we encourage every single member of the team to do that, to welcome change instead of fearing it? How do we ensure that there are no backsliders?"

"There must be no coercion, no manipulation," Kivali replied. "The ethos of the group will determine the prevailing culture. If the Chemistry among the individuals is good and true bonding between each and every one exists, then they will all be empowered to play a leadership role. In that case, it is only necessary for the team leader to apply minor course corrections.

"But if the Chemistry and bonding is weak, the argument that safety can be achieved by reversion to the tried and tested ways of earlier times may prove irresistible. Autocrats and dictators thrive in such an environment."

"At first, I just couldn't see it. Now it seems so clear!" exclaimed Tamias, basking in the pride of discovery.

"I commend You for catching on so quickly," Kivali responded.

Moose ambled over to Kivali and Tamias, deciding to join the discussion. "Let's discuss Chemistry," said Moose gently, without deflating Tamias. "What were the messages of the day for You?"

"You haven't introduced today's P.M. Poser, have You?" Tamias asked. Moose closed his eyes, shaking his head slowly from side to side.

"Then may I put one to You both?" said Tamias, surprised at his own bravura.

This was not the first time Tamias had shown Moose his mettle. Moose liked that, for he had no respect for sycophants. "Pick Your Poser," he invited.

"I have learned that excellent communications and good listening skills are vital components of Chemistry. As You rise in the hierarchy of the organization, You have greater access to information, but, at the same time, it seems more difficult to hear. At Your level, does the honest truth reach You, as it did before?"

"A very good Poser, Tamias. You are right, there is a paradox at work here. The higher up, or more senior You are, the more difficult it is to hear and the less likely You are to hear the truth, especially if it is uncomplimentary or contrary to Your known position. It is at this point that You need good listening skills more than ever before. This leads to

**Moose's Law of Listening: The need for honest listening rises with seniority."**

"But learning the skills necessary to listen well is easy," countered Kivali. "What is much more difficult is the cultivation of a listening attitude, an awareness that listening is a valuable activity. Most of us are addicted to the thrill of listening to ourselves."

"Agreed," Moose said, easing his rear legs into a more comfortable position. "But armed with that listening attitude, we can break through the barriers to maturity and empathy. Once on the other side, we find an understanding that others are important, that they have opinions that matter, that teams cannot be built and organizations cannot succeed until every member listens."

Tamias found that he was listening to himself listening. It reminded him of the inhibiting effect of timing one's breathing. "Suri told me that You must listen with Your nose and Your eyes as well as Your ears, so that You are sensitive to the signals of body language, too."

"I'll wager, Tamias," said Moose, "that You have often heard Customer-People talking to members of the Zoo-Community, but that You have never noticed them *listening* to us. Isn't that remarkable?''

Tamias had never thought about it this way before but he had to admit that Moose was absolutely correct.

"On the other hand," Moose continued, "we can look to the White-tailed Deer to appreciate the value of good listening skills. It has few defenses other than its exceptional listening abilities, but it can shift into speeds of over eighty kilometers per hour at the slightest sound of danger.''

The three fell silent as they mulled over the broad range of concepts they had covered.

Sensing a natural break, Moose made a proposal. "Let's see if we can develop a checklist for successful listening. Tamias, why don't You start?''

Tamias nodded his head thoughtfully, sifting through the choices. ''Well,'' he began, ''I would say that it is important to create the environment in which good listening can take place. No interruptions or distractions, perhaps a change of venue, free of power signals, somewhere that is relaxing. Next, You should clear Your mind, unlink from current crises, cool out, focus on the objectives of the exchange and why You are involved. I would also recommend setting an agenda, some framework for the discussion.''

"Yes, but don't You think it is also important not to

anticipate what we think we will hear?" said Kivali, warming to the subject. "Since we hear seven times faster than we speak, the question for each of us is, 'What do we do in our spare time?' If we are guessing ahead, we will be distracted, bending what we do hear to fit our preconceptions, and perhaps our prejudices."

Moose was enjoying the exchange and decided it would be more instructive for Tamias if he refrained from contributing. Tamias was a good self-teacher.

"When the listening and hearing is done it is wise to restate what You think You heard," Tamias said. "Not just what Your ears heard, but what Your eyes heard, what Your nose heard and, as Suri taught me, the message inherent in body language.

"As You mentioned, Kivali," Tamias continued, "we are more skilled in transmitting than receiving. Perhaps the greatest impediment to good listening is the tendency to rehearse the next grand eloquence while the other party is still speaking!"

Both Tamias and Kivali admitted privately to an occasional fault in this regard. Their silence suggested to Moose that Tamias had touched a nerve, so he diplomatically moved the conversation along.

"Tamias, what messages concerning Chemistry did the Wolves and the Meerkats share with You today?"

"I think there were several. I learned that successful teams don't deal in negatives. They are sparing with negative criticism because it often results in a net loss to both parties, a mutual depletion of the shared Chemistry. Instead, they deliver criticism in a constructive, positive way and they consider stroking, sharing and teaching to be investments in the team that lead to mutual profit.

"They place a high value on the maintenance of a positive attitude and they encourage regular reinforcement of positive self-talk. Mutual celebration is an important feature of successful teams. And to maintain their own motivation, successful team players deliberately distance themselves from the negatives to reduce the danger of their own outlook becoming polluted. These are some of the catalytic techniques used in team-building."

"That should explain to You why Nemesis is the pariah of the Zoo-Community," Moose interjected quietly. "If we let his negative spirit fester, *every one* of us would eventually fail, and therefore the whole organization would fail."

Tamias expressed his agreement with this wise and profound statement with a nod. "Successful teams do not seem to be dominated by any single ego," he said. "I noticed how generous the Meerkats are in sharing power, authority and credit. There seems to exist a kind of matrix of loyalty and commitment, a commitment to the team and to the individual at the same time."

Kivali rose to get another drink from the pond. Then, turning to Tamias, she said, "Moose's ego is as well managed as it is developed. I remember the time when Qing Qing and Quan Quan, the Giant Pandas, arrived at the Zoo-Community. Until that time, we had been the undisputed box-office attractions for Customer-People. Moose just pitched in to help as usual—no animosity or jealousy, just camaraderie. He was a model for every member of the Zoo-Community."

Moose modestly ignored the praise. "I have developed a communication theory that might interest You, Tamias. I call it the Three Level Theory of Communication, because it describes the three different levels of everyday communication.

"*Low Level* is purely *Mechanical*: 'Good morning. How are You?', 'Have a good day,' and so on.

"*Middle Level* is *Prepackaged*, made up of phrases that we have learned: 'That's a very interesting point that You have made,' or 'You are so interesting, I could just go on listening to You all night,' for example.

"Finally, we have *High Level*, the *Visceral* communication that comes from the stomach. *High Level* is the unvarnished, honest, genuine truth. The 'com' in communication means together, and Chemistry is built by the *High Level* communications we have together. Very often it is severely undermined by

*Low* and *Middle Level* communication."

"It would seem to me that *Low* and *Middle Level* communication are pleasant and innocuous enough," observed Tamias. "Don't we all appreciate the effort to project empathy, even if it may be strained or contrived? Don't You also think that it's better to try anything that's positive?"

"Of course. Sometimes any expression of caring is better than no consideration at all. But today we are all better trained and educated than before. Most of us can detect insincerity. These days we are all reaching for higher levels of communication. Today we respect the integrity of communications more than its cosmetic appeal."

Moose stretched and sprang to his feet. "Time to call it a night. You have done very well, Tamias. By studying diligently with our friends, You are learning that leadership is no more, and yet no less, than the practice of the Three Keys of Mastery, Chemistry and Delivery. If each of us takes a few regular steps that lead to improved Mastery, Chemistry and Delivery, we will find the path to personal and organizational symmetry.

"Think about this, Tamias," Moose continued. "Interdependence is at the heart of good Chemistry. Successful teams have learned this lesson. Consider this example. Dolphins depend on voluntary respiration, so they are interdependent in ways in which we aren't: they have a group mind. If a Dolphin loses consciousness for any reason, his friends must wake him up or he'll drown. So all Dolphins are aware of where every other Dolphin is, just in case of an emergency.

"It would appear that their need for this degree of interdependence is greater than ours, but in reality our need to survive is just as powerful a force. Recognition of the importance of interdependence leads to and releases LOVE. Love is nature's second sun. And love creates Chemistry. Good Chemistry is the lifeblood for survival and bonding into successful teams."

In the gloaming, Moose's eyes seemed to burn with the passion of his message. Tamias looked at the two Ghost Tigers and shook his head in admiration. He stood up and said, "Moose, the Wolves taught me the importance of building excellence into teams today. Ulric told me that they have found no shortage of individuals with a strong drive to succeed wishing to join their teams. In my judgment, that's because the Wolves are committed to being a class act. The Zoo-Community is the same. It is a class act, and Your imprint in creating that is everywhere. I'm having a wonderful time learning the Way of the Tiger. I'm grateful to You for inviting me."

Tamias scampered home in the twilight. His heart was singing with joy.

# The
# Third
# Key

# *Delivery*

Finding Customers, both internal and external, identifying their needs and meeting them.

FOURTEEN / IN WHICH *Tamias meets Rosy and Becky the Cape Fur Seals, and learns how to listen to Customer-People and meet their needs.*

s Tamias and Bah-rabar walked down the trail, the Chipmunk strained for a glimpse of the Hippopotamuses, but they were submerged in the mud and water, looking like rocks. Farther along the savannah, Tamias became entranced by the Damara Zebras. They had shadow stripes between their broad black stripes and no stripes at all on their legs.

Bah-rabar resumed his role as tour guide: "Because of their stripes, the Zebras in the circuses of Roman times were called horse-tigers or *Hippotigris*." He flicked his crown of feathers in a gesture of erudition.

They continued along the trail past the Cheetahs. Tamias had never met them. Bah-rabar continued his running commentary. "The Cheetah is the Master of speed, the fastest land mammal on Earth. Over short distances, they can reach speeds of up to one hundred and twenty-five kilometers per hour." Tamias thought the black lines running down beneath their eyes, like inky tear stains, made them look sad.

Next Bah-rabar introduced Tamias to the Springbucks. "They 'pronk,'" said Bah-rabar.
"Pardon?" said Tamias.

Bah-rabar addressed the closest Springbuck. "Excuse me Dorcas, would You mind pronking for my friend Tamias?"

The closest Springbuck obligingly leaped three meters straight up in the air without flexing her legs. "*That's* called pronking!" said Bah-rabar.

As they rounded the last part of the trail, Tamias could hear the hoarse barking of the Cape Fur Seals. "You won't have a lot of time with the Seals, Tamias," Bah-rabar was saying, "because they perform every lunchtime at eleven o'clock."

After Bah-rabar departed, Tamias climbed up the fencing that enclosed the Seals' pond, dropping onto one of the rocks on the other side. He felt as though he had surprised them in their boudoir—all the Seals were grooming themselves. They had emerged from the water, shaken their bodies and now were scratching themselves with the nail-like claws of their hind feet.

Many were grooming their fur with their forefeet and then rolling onto their backs, rubbing themselves against the jagged surface of the rocks. Others re-entered the water, swimming on their backs as they rubbed their cheeks and faces from ears to nose, rolling slowly in lazy spirals.

As if suddenly becoming aware of their visitor, the rest of the Seals took to the pool, their splashing and swimming erupting everywhere. Their water-slicked coats were dark gray-brown with reddish underfur. Exaggerated white whiskers bristled from their faces and big, brown, mischievous eyes stole frequent, self-conscious glances at Tamias.

The Seals swam in every body position: on their bellies, on their backs, some of them twirling as they advanced through the water. Some jumped and splashed at each other, while others leaped out of the water in pairs, Dolphin style, plunging underwater at speeds of four meters per second.

What a demonstration of Mastery, the perfect harmony of physique with environment, resulting in a unique beauty of movement. These submarine paddlers, Tamias thought, were *built* for water sports!

As the Seals swam, many seemed to have developed a routine. First they would erupt through the water's surface, then make an arching turn, then dive headlong to the bottom again, trailing a row of bubbles from each nostril.

As usual, Tamias found himself so engrossed with the talents of team members that he became oblivious to time and objective. He was startled by a Seal streaking clean out of the water right under his nose. The Seal honked at him in mid-air:

> *"Hello there, Tammy. I'm glad to meet You.*
> *Moose has arranged for us to greet You."*

Then she disappeared into the deep again. Another seemed to rise from the same watery hole. During her turn she told Tamias:

> *"And another Hello! so glad You're here!*
> *I'm Becky, that's Rosy—lend us Your ear!"*

"Er, I've come to learn the Key of Delivery from You," said Tamias uncertainly, trying to catch her on her next loop. Everywhere Seals seemed to be popping in and out of the water.

Tamias watched the water anxiously. Suddenly, Becky knifed through the surface:

> *"Remember, the purpose of what You're at*
> *Is not to make You a big fat cat."*

Rosy broke into the air, completing the thought:

> *"The selling of smiles is what we all do,*
> *To Customer-People (C-Ps to You)."*

Then Becky emerged again:

> *"Just listen to all that C-Ps may say,*
> *And then, my friend, do it all their way."*

Followed by Rosy:

> *"Meet C-Ps' needs like a critter possessed,*
> *By doing the things that You do best."*

Then it was Becky's turn:

> *"Be kind to Yourself by meeting each need*
> *Of Customer-People; that's Your creed."*

The waters stopped churning. Tamias searched for Rosy and Becky but the water near him was still and clear. They must have swum in another direction, he thought. He was standing on the edge of the rock, almost falling into the water.

Tamias could swim but he wasn't about to get messed up on the last day of his Masterclass, so he made a strategic retreat and sat on his haunches a safe distance from the water's edge. Then Becky emerged:

> *"Sorry to say, but we've gotta go now,*
> *It's show-biz time; gotta get our chow."*

Then Rosy:

> *"We'll swim in circles and jump for lunch,*
> *To win smiles and happiness from that bunch."*

Becky again:

> *"So thanks, Good Buddy, for lending Your ear,*

*Give our regards to the Great White Bear."*

Rosy:

*"From what we have seen, You'll fit in just fine,
So we'll share with You our bottom line."*

Then both of them together:

*"What smart critters know in a biz with fizz,
Is what the C-P sees, IS WHAT IS!"*

Then they were gone, swimming to the far side of
the pool where a feeder was drawing Pilchards,
Squid, Mackerel and Herring from a bucket and
throwing them into the air. Customer-People had
come to enjoy smiles, giggles, applause and rapture.
At eleven o'clock that morning, there were more
snowballs in Hell than frowns at the Cape Fur Seal
pool.

FIFTEEN / IN WHICH *Tamias meets Bisitik, Kunik and Sanikaluaq the Polar Bears, from whom he learns the importance of being consistent and thorough, the value of feedback and the benefits of the Itch and Scratch Theory of Delivery.*

he Giraffes lived next door to the Cape Fur Seals. To Tamias they looked like walking trees. He was entranced, having never seen a living thing so high.

Bah-rabar decided to enlighten his furry friend. "The ancestry of Giraffes, and their cousins the Okapi, dates back fifteen million years. Julius Caesar first introduced them into Zoos forty-six years before Christ was born; they were called 'Camel Leopards.' That is why they are known today by the Latin name *Giraffa camelopardalis.*"

Biology is not a science, thought Tamias; it is the art of ridiculing creatures in Latin. But as usual he was impressed by the richness of Bah-rabar's Zoological knowledge, and he appreciated his friend's knack for the curious.

Tamias had discovered the blue footprints painted on the path that led to the Polar Bears. Feigning mastery of the complex Zoo-Community geography, he assumed the lead. As they approached the Americas Restaurant, Bah-rabar excused himself to join his friends for lunch. Tamias continued on to the Polar Bears.

As he climbed up the hill, a sonorous melody of grunts and sighs caught his ears. He scooted between the Customer-People, who were waiting patiently for feeding time, and over the concrete walls surrounding the Polar Bears' pool.

Lost in the ecstasy of a glorious backscratching session was a great she-Bear named Bisitik (Inuit for "hero"). Balancing her two-hundred-and-seventy-kilo hulk uncertainly on her back feet, she slowly eased her back up and down the sharp edges of the gray, angular rocks. *"Ooooooh! Aaah! Mmmm-mnnn!"* she grunted and gnarred in delirium.

Sanikaluaq ("fast runner") swam to the edge of the pool and climbed out onto the rocks. The water cascaded from her shaggy coat, forming great puddles at her paws. "Hi! Tamias! Glad to meet Ya! Do me a favor—stand back behind that rock for a moment, will Ya?" As Tamias ran for cover, she shook her waterlogged body, drenching the spot where he had stood.

"That's better. Now where'd Ya go? Oh! There You

are. Boy, You sure are small! Better not get under my feet or You'll be an ex-Chipmunk. Ha! Ha! Ha!"

Tamias failed to see the humor in Sanikaluaq's remark, but her advice was impeccable!

"Nothin' likc a good ol' scratch, right Tam?"

Tamias agreed. He took a good look at this giant white nomad that the Inuit call "ah-tik-tok," or "those who go down to the sea." Sanikaluaq had a deep chest and shoulders—and a big bottom, too, thought Tamias, a little irreverently. Her head was long and narrow with small, rounded ears. She had beautiful brown eyes, but strangely, it seemed to Tamias at least, no eyelashes. Her nose and parts of her lips and claws were brown-black and white whiskers sprouted from her upper lip. Polar Bears are so big that their cubs must run beside their mothers, to avoid stumbling in Mama's footprints. We're talking *big*, thought Tamias.

"*Ooooooh! Aaa-rrrggghh! Hhhh-mmmmmmnnn!*" Tamias looked over at Bisitik, who was still deep in the throes of hedonistic backscratching.

"Tam, I'm no philosopher or deep thinker," said Sanikaluaq. "I leave that stuff to the likes of Dinding and Moose. But I want to leave a message with You. See Bisitik over there?"

Tamias nodded.

"She's got an itch. Right now, the biggest thing on her mind is to get the pesky thing scratched." Sanikaluaq had fishy breath, which, unfortunately for Tamias, she exhaled into his face as she spoke. "From now on, I want You to think of all Customer-People that way. They come to You with an itch. Your job is to scratch. Simple as that!"

"Can You elaborate for me?" asked Tamias, trying discreetly to establish some distance between them.

"Sure!" Sanikaluaq said with a broad smile. "See all those Customer-People over there? They've come here to watch Bisitik and Kunik and me have lunch." Then, pointing with her nose in the direction of the Customer-People, she asked Tamias, "What's their itch?"

Tamias thought for a moment, and then answered, "To smile, to have fun, to entertain their young."

"You've got it! How will we scratch that itch?"

"By displaying Your swimming and running skills and showing off for the Customer-People?"

"You've got it again, little brother! Let me show Ya how it's done."

The viewing area was crowded with Customer-People, who were buzzing with anticipation. An expectant hush fell upon them as a young Keeper-Person with green coveralls and long red hair strode to the feeding platform. In his right hand he carried a bucket from which he began to toss fish into the air. The great white Bears paced themselves, building the suspense for the Customer-People. They ambled over to the fish as they landed, munching them casually on the spot. The Customer-People smiled and chuckled with delight as each fish was despatched.

The time had come to increase the pace. The Keeper-Person started to throw the fish into the water. The big male Bear called Kunik (Inuit for "kiss") was the first to dive into the crystal-clear blue waters, quickly followed by the two she-Bears.

Beneath the surface, the Bears came into their own, displaying their natural grace by churning through the water as they twisted and turned in pursuit of each fishy treat. Their aquatic skills attracted more Customer-People to the submarine viewing area where they could watch the performance from a new perspective. They saw a mere glimpse of a Bear glancing off the glass walls of the pool, and then a floating mass of white fur, and next, a driving force of bubbles and fur hurtling towards them, eyes open and front legs outstretched.

Kunik demonstrated his push-off abilities, pressing his feet against the glass. The Customer-People could see that his forefeet were broader than his rear feet, with half the length of the toes covered with a swimming membrane. Except for the balls of his feet, the soles were covered with hair, for traction in snowy terrain.

The show was soon over but the faces of every last

Customer-Person were dressed with smiles. The Keeper-Person picked up his empty bucket and the happy Customer-People dispersed, chattering and chuckling to each other. The Bears trod water while they snapped up any remaining morsels.

Sanikaluaq climbed out of the pool and padded across the granite. Tamias headed for the protection of the large rocks before the anticipated deluge.

As Tamias emerged, Sanikaluaq said, "Well, little guy, do Ya get the Itch 'n' Scratch picture?"

Tamias nodded.

"We're no Einsteins around here, but we sure know how to deliver the highest standards of Mastery and Chemistry for the Customer-People, and we don't do so bad either—we get lunch! If it's raining, we go into the pool so Customer-People can watch us from under cover. Customer-People don't like rain, Ya know. Ya gotta see things from the Customer-People's point of view. That's what Dinding calls 'feedback' and some other big word."

"Cybernetics?" asked Tamias politely.

"Yeah! That's it, cybermatics. But Ya gotta be sure not to miss any itchy part. Consistency, it's called."

Two Customer-People arrived at the fence. The young one was screaming its head off and the big one was getting very bad-tempered. "Whoops! Gotta go now, Tamias. See Ya around, eh?"

The three great white Bears dove into the blue

waters, chasing each other and performing their maneuvers. Magic! The frowns and wails of the Customer-People melted into smiles.

SIXTEEN / IN WHICH *Tamias meets Din-ding, the Orang-utan and great Philosopher, discussing with him the compound value of Delivery; the effect of self-esteem; goal-setting from the Customer-Person's perspective; and Customer-People as a valuable research resource.*

ah-rabar and Tamias took the Round the World Tour Trail over the bridge that crosses the Serpentine, past the Australasian Pavilion and through the meadows. Bah-rabar went ahead as Tamias paused to eat a meadow-grass seed. Suddenly he was gripped by an unexplainable and urgent sense of danger. He bolted into the dank cavity of a rotten sycamore.

Overhead circled the silhouette most feared by all Chipmunks, the one-and-a-half-meter wingspan of a Red-tailed Hawk. The single most important lesson taught to Tamias by his mother was for a dangerous moment like this: that he should always remain in the protection of a sanctuary until he had counted to one hundred, and, she had stressed, that the counting should *never* start until the imprisonment has become unbearable.

Now, in this moment of peril, he obeyed her dictum as faithfully as if she were standing by his side.

". . .ninety-nine, one hundred." He poked a whisker outside. Peeping farther, he scanned the sky. A flurry of Pine Siskins, in bursts of up-and-down, headed south to their winter home, singing their songs of twangy syllables on the wing. In the other direction, a Yellow Warbler was "buzzing" a Crow from its territory. But fortunately for Tamias, his enemy by now had become just a memory.

Tamias caught up with Bah-rabar. "Sorry about that," he said in the most casual tone he could muster.

As they walked silently together towards the Indo-Malaya Pavilion, Bah-rabar, oblivious of the drama but sensing that Tamias was upset, thoughtfully provided him with a moment or two to regain his composure.

"Tamias," Bah-rabar said after a discreet interlude, "I am going to tell You a story. Many seasons ago, a Chimpanzee was sitting beside an Orang-utan at the river's edge. With his finger, he drew a small circle in the mud. 'That represents what the Orang-utan knows,' he said. Then he drew a much larger circle around the first one and bragged, 'This represents what the Chimpanzee knows.'

"The Orang-utan stared at the two circles in the mud for several moments before observing, 'It is often said that the Chimpanzee is the smartest primate, so You may be right.' Then, with his finger, he drew a third circle, as far as he could reach, and this one surrounded the first two. 'We should remember,' he said gently, 'this is what neither of us knows.'"

The two walked silently for several meters. Tamias sifted through the parable's many nuances before asking, "Is there another reason, besides the obvious one, for telling me this story?"

"There is indeed," said Bah-rabar. "Your Tutorial on Delivery today is going to be with Dinding, the senior Orang-utan of the Zoo-Community, not Moose. 'Orang-utan,' by the way, is a Malayan word which means 'Man of the Woods.' Dinding enjoyed a very successful tenure as Moose's predecessor and is revered by all the members of the Zoo-Community. He is a scholar and philosopher and he has studied the world for more than thirty years. Some underestimate him. This is unwise, for he has great wisdom and long experience of the Three Keys of the Zoo-Community."

"Thank You for the advice."

Shrugging, as if it was all in a day's work, Bah-rabar continued, "I'm going over now to see Charles the Gorilla and his boys. As You may know, they are Delivery experts, and they have developed a new

Customer-People-pleaser. It seems that they acquired a cutdown plastic oil drum, which Charles places on the ground. He then bends over it, resting his hands on the upper surface. Holding that posture, he 'drives' it as fast as he can to the most distant end of his home, making as much noise as possible, while his teammates leap out of his way in all directions. This new show is getting rave reviews. I am going to discuss it with him. When Dinding finishes his Tutorial, please join us and I will go with You to Your closing Tutorial with Moose."

A wall of oppressive humidity hit Tamias as he stepped inside the Indo-Malaya Pavilion. Simians and avians were locked in what seemed to be a vocal competition, *fortissimo*. It was a wonder the hibiscus blooms could maintain their serenity in such a din.

Tamias scooted past the Ring-necked Parakeets and the Greater Hill Mynahs, waving to Raja and Rani as he passed their home again. As he careened around the corner, he was presented with the matronly appearance of Abigail, an Orang-utan from Sumatra who had seen twenty-nine summers. Although the recent mother of Dinar, today she was flirting with one of the Customer-People. Pursing her lips, she planted them on the armored glass and surprised the small visitor with a vacuum-powered kiss, the loudest he had heard in all his young life. After a while she became bored by the one-sidedness of the affair and loped off to join her son.

Tamias intercepted her. "Excuse me, but can You tell me where Dinding is?"

Abigail raised her long arm and pointed to the sky.

"He hasn't, uh, died, has he?" Tamias asked.

Abigail pointed, with a little more accuracy, to a platform five meters above the ground. There sat Dinding, a great, venerable male, covered in distinctive reddish-brown hair. His cheeks bulged out in flat, gray, fleshy lobes, and large pouches hung from his throat like multiple double chins, which extended down his chest, across into his armpits and right over his back to his shoulder blades. These were resonators, used for voice amplification when Dinding emitted his *long-call*, a three-minute sequence of sighs and groans.

Tamias climbed up the metal and wood structure and Dinding rose to greet him. Weighing a massive one hundred and fifty kilos, he was more than one-and-a-half meters tall, with an arm-span of two-and-a-half meters.

"Pleased to meet You, Tamias." Dinding delivered his gruff but friendly greeting and immediately collapsed like a great Buddha into his former lotus position.

Tamias wondered if Moose would have described "Pleased to meet You" as Lower or Middle Level Communication.

Dinding held his arms up to the sky and stared into the air.

"When You were watching Abigail, Tamias, You were witnessing a Master of Delivery in the act of creating synergy with Customer-People. You see, every smile we put on the face of a Customer-Person is a victory for us. But smiles delivered separately are not as valuable as two that follow each other, the second nourished by the warmth of the first. Have You ever noticed that Your second smile is always wider than the first, if it follows immediately? The moral, therefore, is that Delivery must be consistent and frequent. Customer-People have a greater sense that their needs are being met if You do it consistently, building on each success."

Dinding turned to Tamias. Bringing his hands to rest in his lap, he asked rather absent-mindedly, "Do You think we could bottle the smiles and laughter of young Customer-People and sell them?"

Without waiting for a reply, Dinding continued, "It is a paradox that Customer-People believe that they are the most intelligent beings on our Earth because they *can't* talk to anyone else. So, too, do we usually try to see everything from our own perspectives."

Dinding permitted himself a smile. Tamias smiled, too. The Philosopher-Orang-utan, pleased with this silent tribute to his wit, continued his reflections: "But Customer-People are not to be manipulated into the limits of our understanding. Our understanding must be released and expanded to accommodate the needs of Customer-People, as those needs are discovered."

Dinding paused and then shot a question at the Chipmunk. "How would You achieve that, Tamias?"

Tamias was daydreaming about these concepts. The abruptness with which the question was delivered almost made him fall off the platform. He gathered his thoughts, knowing that this would not be a good moment to drop a blooper.

"I think," he said after some consideration, "that most of the time we are afraid to ask Customer-People to specify their needs. Yet, it seems obvious to me, the provider must always ask Customer-People to define their needs before trying to meet them. This must be done at both the individual and general levels."

"So true, so true. I like Your focus on Customer-People. So far during Your Masterclass, You may only have heard the term 'Customer-People' used in its narrower meaning. But I prefer a wider definition. Customers are all those who come to us with a need. Family, friends, lovers, buyers, suppliers, colleagues: all those with whom we share a relationship based on interdependence. They all have itches which we must scratch. It's our job to be their dream-makers, to help them realize their wish-list."

"That is a very elegant idea, Dinding," replied Tamias. He was enjoying this exchange as much as Dinding was.

Tamias decided to introduce another theme that had been exercising his mind. "I also believe that we waste too much time in mass-market researching of Customer-People. Usually they either don't really know what they want or they will provide the answers they think are expected of them. Instead we should watch and listen to them, one-on-one, and ask *them* to design the product or service. If we ask a Customer-Person how we can provide a better service, new approaches and innovation will result. They represent a free research and development source, and it's probably the best we can get.

"This is what happened earlier today when I was with the Polar Bears. They had designed their architecture of satisfaction from the Customer-Peoples' perspective, not their own. They promoted the Itch and Scratch Model of Customer feedback and satisfaction. They were Customer-driven, not provider-driven. Their enjoyment came from meeting the needs of Customer-People, a kind of self-enlightened altruism in which they gave in order to receive, and their most cherished reward was a psychic one."

Dinding inflated his resonator and slowly released the air, causing several short bubbling sighs, followed by some grunts, squeaks, hoots and a sucking noise made through his pursed lips. He sounded like a drunken Elephant. It was his way of saying he liked Tamias's approach!

"Bravo!" he exclaimed. "As You know, You are, in effect, describing Moose's Law of Enlightened Self-Interest. But how does one justify the concept of altruism and generosity without sacrifice, giving in order that one may receive?"

"By demonstrating the practical benefits!" Tamias responded. "Too often we focus on the *process*, not the *needs*. Yet, as we know, if You would take from a thing, You must first give to it. It is more effective to satisfy one's own needs by first satisfying those of Customer-People. This is the Cybernetic Model of Customer Satisfaction, or the Itch and Scratch Model, if You prefer. Customer-People define their needs. You meet them. They reward and celebrate You. You continue to meet their needs and they continue to reward and celebrate You. This process can continue indefinitely. In an organization in which this culture prevails, things get done and everyone wins. In fact, it's the only way in which everyone *can* win."

It was not often that the great Philosopher of Delivery was treated with such a gifted and promising pupil. "Continue, continue! Please!" he encouraged, closing his eyes to increase his acuity.

"Delivery should embody the essence of satisfaction, it should never be superficial or mechanical. Abigail has just demonstrated that point so well. She was celebrating the Customer. She was marketing, not selling. She was displaying warmth, bonding and Chemistry with the Customer-Person."

"Moose by now has explained his Three Level Theory of Communication?" Dinding inquired, opening one eye.

Tamias nodded.

"Applying his theory to giving, do You think Low and Middle Level giving is appropriate? Or must all giving only be undertaken at the High Level?"

"During my Masterclass," replied Tamias, "I have formed the opinion that the ultimate morality is to fulfill Yourself, in every way. Of course, this may only be done by means that do not harm or exploit others, but help them. High Level giving to Customer-People is the ideal, but as You and I both know, rarely are things found in their ideal state. I am inclined to think that Moose is an exception, because he appears to teach from the heart, with the care and love of a doting parent. He is 'reaching', not 'teaching.'"

"I think You may be overlooking an important ingredient in Delivery," said Dinding, "and that is the concept of self-esteem. Because Abigail respects herself, others respect her. The most important thing in Delivery is the existence of self-esteem.

Until this feeling is pre-eminent, nothing else matters, because what we feel about ourselves is what
we project and give to others.

"If You don't like what You do and You don't feel good
about Yourself, You can be sure that Manager-People
and Customer-People will read You; they won't feel
good about themselves, and therefore about the Zoo-
Community, either. If this is their perception, they
won't return and the opportunity to define needs and
meet them will never again be presented!"

With this, Dinding suddenly swung over the edge
of his platform, hanging upside down from a bar by
his feet, while his body remained upright. The liga-
ments of his hip joints were so long and loose that he
was able to put his legs to one side above his head, in
an angle that seemed, to Tamias, painfully impos-
sible. He placed his hands on his ample belly and
began to meditate, mumbling something about people, Kaizen, strength, the unlimited power of "You"
and love.

## SEVENTEEN / IN WHICH *Tamias meets Nemesis for the last time and challenges him to a duel.*

Concluding
that his Tu-
torial with
Dinding
must be
over,
Tamias
ran down
the platform
struts and
dropped
to the
ground.
He
waved
goodbye to
Abigail and
Dinar and
sprinted
past the
Gibbons.
"Hey!
Dude!"
he heard
Lenny call,
but as he didn't
have time to
stop, he
merely squeaked
a hasty greeting
in response.
As he
raced
past the
Sailfin
Lizard
and the

Star Tortoise, a familiar, clammy chill embraced him. "Hello, Tamias-s-s, my friend. I do hope that you have seen the light of reason and decided to join my team."

Tamias turned. The head and spread hood of the Spectacled Cobra swayed from side to side as Nemesis's expressionless black eyes mesmerized him into a listless, feeble state.

"You are probably finding the enemies of administration to be the very nicest of creatures. Is that not s-s-so, Tamias-s-s?" The Chipmunk could barely hear the hypnotic hiss of sedition.

Even as he felt his unsteadiness grow, Tamias realized that he had to break Nemesis's ability to influence and manipulate his attitudes and goals. It would have to be a duel of minds. The Serpent had perfected the art of intellectual seduction through the use of persuasive argument, and Tamias knew that his sole defense would have to be superior reason.

Nemesis's head stopped swaying, becoming as still as death. He sensed a loosening of his control over Tamias. "Tamias-s-s, I want you to dream with me for a moment about a better Zoo-Community, in which the needs of our members hold s-s-sway over the needs of Customer-People. This will be a brave new world in which your and my needs will come first for a change. We will put an end to the domination of the Zoo-Community by Customer-People!"

Tamias recalled his meeting with Suri the Meerkat and how she had taught him to retune his self-talk. Suri's words rang in his ears: "Dangers, disappointments and defeats have to be overcome, walked away from, detoured, forgotten or accepted." Well, this danger was one he would not accept! This was the time to put Suri's techniques to the test. Tamias avoided the Snake's malevolent gaze while he conducted his internal dialogue, refining and rebuilding his self-talk. He painted a mental picture of his victory over Nemesis, using the mental imaging technique he had learned from Vulpes the Red Fox, who called it "visioning."

Then, drawing a deep breath, he turned to Nemesis and said, "At every intersection on the path to progress, every innovative spirit is met by a host of Serpents, like You, who wish to defend the past. But I prefer the promise of the future to the comforts of the past. We should favor the errors of enthusiasm and passion rather than the safety and predictability of order and regulation. We need to place less emphasis on efficiency, productivity, administration and control, putting more emphasis on skill, teamwork, making Customer-People smile and, above all, enhancing the quality of our environment and our work life. This is the best way to achieve an improvement in performance. Your lowly vision cannot vault us to greatness."

Nemesis flinched and cringed as if stung by each verbal missile until, lowering his head, he hissed, "You may feel that my ideas are lower than yours, Tamias-s-s, but remember that the great rivers and s-s-seas of Nature s-s-swell because they are lower than myriad lesser streams. In the s-s-same way, I and my friends will prevail here."

"Nemesis," Tamias replied, "to me the word 'friend' is another term for lover, brother, sister, colleague, and team member. We all depend upon these friends and their friendship to ensure that our lives and our organizations sing. For You, the word means those You can manipulate, exploit and control."

Nemesis knew that he was done for, that he had dueled and lost. His plan to recruit a new disciple lay in ruins. As rage devoured him, he lashed his head through the air. Then, lowering his hood and flicking his black slippery tongue through his never-smiling lips, he whispered, "Remember, it is a privilege to command the position that is embraced by the majority, even though it may be manifestly wrong. I shall always be waiting for you, trying to recruit you to my team."

Without acknowledging Nemesis's threat, Tamias turned towards the doors that would lead him to Bahrabar. The adrenalin was still pumping through his body as he recalled the verse of a great American poet:

> ... *Never met this fellow,*
> *Attended or alone,*
> *Without a tighter breathing*
> *And zero at the bone.*

Tamias was cool in more ways than one!

EIGHTEEN / IN WHICH *Moose conducts the fourth and final Tutorial, focusing on making better recruiting decisions; the importance of finding, training and motivating successful team members; how creativity is preceded by destruction; the value of development; the secondary nature of profit; aesthetics in organizations; and the Laws of Recruitment, Bureaucracy, Leadership and Assets.*

vents in the Zoo-Community don't remain private for very long with a gossip like Melos the Song Sparrow in residence. Melos had a keen sense of rumor! Today he could hardly control himself as he chattered and whistled his song of celebration.

"Tamias told Nemesis! Tamias told Nemesis! Tamias told Nemesis!" he warbled. As Bah-rabar walked through the woods and past the Pony Rides, Melos swooped and twittered over his head:

*"Tamias is cool!*

*Tamias is neat!*
*Tamias has bad Nemesis beat!''*

Then he flew over to relay the news to the Barbary Apes and the European Bison.

Bah-rabar and Tamias approached the Boardwalk from opposite directions. "What's this I hear?'' Bah-rabar asked as they met. "Did You and Nemesis have words?''

"Well, we had something of a disagreement, a difference of opinion, You might say!''

"As we all know, Tamias, in reality, everything that exists is a matter of opinion. Melos tells me that You challenged Nemesis to a duel and won. Congratulations!''

"Thank You!'' said Tamias, basking in Bah-rabar's High Level Communication.

"The Zoo-Community is buzzing with the news,'' Bah-rabar said with obvious relish, as they arrived at the Great Maple Tree. "Let's go see Moose and Kivali.'' Bah-rabar took the hillside trail to the forest floor, while Tamias scurried down the familiar, gnarled trunk.

Moose and Kivali showed their pleasure at seeing Tamias with the warmth of their greeting.

"Well, Tamias!'' said the Zoo-Guru, "welcome to our home again. I hear You routed Nemesis this afternoon. Please accept my congratulations!''

"We did not agree on one or two points," said Tamias modestly.

"'Agreement' is just another word for the echo of Your own opinion, Tamias, and Nemesis's opinion of work and life was not echoed by You. The enemies of change and evolution, like Nemesis, are everywhere. They have yet to learn that until no river runs and no tree stands, today must give way to tomorrow's joy.

"All creative acts are preceded by destruction. Every new season in our environment at the Zoo-Community is created from the decay and the remnants of the past, and You will be an important contributor to this process. Some of the seeds that You bury and store will nourish You and Your family when the snow covers the ground. But many others will become the saplings that create and renew our forests. The members of the Zoo-Community, and our friends, will depend on You for ozone, air purification, shade and ground-cover."

Tamias gulped. Had he heard correctly? "You will be an important contributor"?

"Oh! Yes! You have successfully completed the Masterclass, Tamias," said Moose. "But the decision whether You join the Zoo-Community isn't mine alone."

Tamias's elation was suddenly tinged with unease. "Who else must help You decide?" he asked.

"The Masterclass has three objectives," Moose replied. "The first is to inform You of our culture, which we call the Three Keys of Mastery, Chemistry and Delivery. During three Tutorials with Kivali and me, and one with Dinding, You have demonstrated Your enlightenment.

"The second objective was to test Your mettle. Nemesis offered You a different set of values and attitudes and You showed that stubborn custom has no fence against an innovative, open mind and a loving heart.

"And now we come to the third objective. We know that Your attitude, intelligence and skills will be welcomed by all of the team members of the Zoo-Community. But it is just as important that we are right for You as it is that You are right for us. Most organizations commit the error of relying on one-way communication and work with the faulty assumption that recruiting and selection is a one-way process. But as stated in

**Moose's Law of Recruitment: Superstars are not selected by organizations; organizations are selected by superstars.**

"And so, the last step in Your Masterclass reverses our roles: You will interview me, and You will then determine if You want me and the members of the Zoo-Community to be a part of Your consciousness."

Tamias pondered this last challenge, considering which issues interested him most. Then he asked, "The Three Keys seem to be very easy to understand and practice. How were so many complicated ideas distilled into just three fundamentals?"

"All great ideas are easy to understand once they have been discovered," replied Moose. "The hard part is to discover them. By working together, combining all our strengths and listening, we learned that there are differences between quantity and quality, between growth and development, between size and beauty. We learned that the only visible difference between a dead cactus and a living one is that the living one is growing. We learned that profit is like oxygen: vital for our survival but not the purpose of our existence, because what we become is more important than how much we profit materially."

Moose padded across the grass to the water's edge to slake his thirst. The others followed his example. Moose licked the water droplets from his whiskers as he framed his next thoughts carefully in his beautiful mind.

"In this sense, most organizations are aesthetically deficient; they are like a magnificent blossom without perfume. Yet *aesthetics is the single most important issue facing us all*. We all want to work in a place that is fun and attractive, where our colleagues are stimulating and friendly, where the tasks are dignifying and worthwhile and where the pay-off consists of both psychic and material rewards." Moose lashed his tail for emphasis.

"We discovered that we can best inspire successful team members—that is, lovers, brothers, sisters, colleagues and any others upon whom we depend— through beauty, truth, recreation and creation. The Masterful execution of a craft is a beautiful thing to see, to touch, to hear, to smell, to taste. Perfect Chemistry is a beautiful sensation. The act of Delivering a scratch to a Customer-Person's itch is a beautiful moment. Forged together, the resulting symmetry and beauty is so powerful that a constant flow of enthusiasts seek to share and contribute to the beauty we have created here.

"From this, we discovered the natural corollary. Administration becomes a secondary issue in an organization where Customer-People love what You do, keep coming back for more, tell their friends about You and make Your profits grow every season. From this, I have formulated

**Moose's Law of Bureaucracy: In an organization enjoying a rising tide of happy Customers, administration is a secondary function."**

"Even Confucius practiced the Way of the Tiger, living by Delivery, Chemistry and Mastery, saying,

'Each day I examine myself thrice: Have I been faithful in serving others? Have I been honest with my friends? Have I reviewed the Master's lessons?''

Tamias had experienced this very excitement. He had already been infused by a sense of pride and joy through his classes with all of his new friends at the Zoo-Community. He wondered, though, if Bah-rabar, Dinding, Kivali and Moose were at a different level.

"This philosophy may work well for the majority of team members," he said, "but how does it affect the organization's structure and how is leadership practiced in a work environment like the Zoo-Community?"

"The meaning of leadership has changed dramatically over the years," replied Moose. "Not long ago, only Manager-People did the managing and leading; but not any more! Most forward-thinking organizations today have come to resemble the Zoo-Community. Their units are dispersed, their structures are leaner, their levels are less stratified and they lack traditional hierarchies. Today we are better educated, more aware and self-directed and hungrier for autonomy. For these reasons and because of increasing specialization, Manager-People cannot and do not need to understand how every part of the organization works. Manager-People no longer 'help' us by making our decisions or solving our problems. We have learned that problems can only be absolved, resolved, solved or dissolved by each one of us, at every level. As You will have learned from the Meerkats, leadership is now a universal function. And as You will have observed throughout Your Masterclass, every team member in the Zoo-Community has leadership skills and uses them to varying degrees and in unique ways. This is

**Moose's Law of Leadership: A successful team with one hundred members has one hundred leaders."**

Moose selected a cool, green patch of grass and fell over on his side with a thump. Kivali, Bah-rabar and Tamias rearranged their positions accordingly. Moose soused his paw with several licks from a long, pink tongue and spruced up his ears.

"But now we come back to the beginning again, because a leader can't do anything without good team members. No amount of leadership, material resources, organizational culture or structure can compensate for weak or incompetent colleagues. The most important aspects of leadership are those we have been conducting with You for the last three days: finding, training and motivating members of the team and creating an environment in which the Three Keys can be practiced to perfection."

Tamias reflected on Moose's incontestable wisdom, and then observed, "During our second Tutorial, we talked about the importance of having the right equipment. Afterwards, I discussed this with a friend of mine, Bill the Hairy Woodpecker. If You were to meet Bill, You'd marvel that such a small head could store such a big tongue. I had always admired his ability to chisel into trees to reach hard-to-get grubs.

"Perhaps You already knew this, but he explained his secret to me. His tongue is actually quite short, but it is part of an apparatus of bones and elastic tissue that goes under the jaw and up around the back of his head, anchoring itself in his right nostril, leaving the left one for breathing. Bill releases this apparatus, known as the hyoid, by sliding it around his head, enabling him to protrude his tongue a remarkable distance. Isn't it possible that even experts like Bill cannot optimize their effectiveness without the right equipment?"

Moose shook his great square head, his jowls swinging from side to side. "I only half agree with this idea, because I know that if You practice the Three Keys, You will find the equipment. The Wood-pecker Finch often uses a twig to probe for insects that have retreated into a crevice or hole in a tree. Sometimes he will not only find the tool, but manu-facture it, too, by stripping its leaves off, thus ensur-ing that it will fit into the opening. There are many other examples, such as the Egyptian Turkey Vulture, who uses stones to smash Ostrich eggs, and the Leaf-cutter Ant, who severs sections of leaves, stacking them into structures that will grow sufficient fungi to feed a whole colony. I believe that Bahrabar told You how Charles the Gorilla uses half a plastic oil drum to entertain Customer-People?"

Tamias nodded.

"Talented and well-motivated team members will find every means to exploit their talent, and this will often require the acquisition and use of the finest equipment. Indeed, as long as our team consists of superstars and loyal Customer-People, we will always be able to find any other assets that we need: skills, money, equipment, financing, property, whatever. This is

**Moose's Law of Assets: Superior organizations possess only two major assets: employees and Customers. All other assets automatically follow."**

"Do You have a checklist, or a set of rules, for individual and organizational success?" Tamias asked Moose.

Moose allowed himself a grin. "Perfection lives within imperfection. There is no checklist. There are no 'one-minute' solutions, no lists, no tablets of stone. We have shared with you the Three Level Theory of Communication; the Seven Skills of the

Trainer; the eleven Laws which we call Moose's Moxie; and the Three Keys of Mastery, Chemistry and Delivery. This is our philosophy, our culture. The daily, diligent practice of these ideas is a noble activity that will lead to matchless performance and eventually, therefore, *You will need no rules*.

"When You know that You can do one thing well, You will know that You can do anything. As You excel, and as Your team succeeds, others will say, 'It just happened, they got lucky.' The more You practice the Three Keys, the luckier You will get."

Tamias heard the distant trumpeting of Tequila the Elephant. It was a friendly, welcoming sound. While the fanfare still hung in the air, Jackie and Mandy started their Mandrills' welcome, a chant of screeching and shrieking. Then he heard the welcome of Ulric and his howling team. A great wave of welcoming sounds, from warbling to wailing, bellowing to baying, and snapping to snorting, reached every crevice and corner of the Zoo-Community.

As the vocal pageant reached its crescendo, Tamias could just barely hear that Moose, Kivali and Bah-rabar had joined in, too. Tears of joy filled Tamias's eyes as, with great affection and appreciation, he recalled the first time he had heard that *Kee-rah!* sound. He was certain now that Bah-rabar would be his mentor.

They had all risen in tribute to Tamias, and as the

tattoo of welcome subsided, Moose turned to Tamias. "As You have just heard, Your invitation to become a permanent member of the team we call the Zoo-Community is unanimous. The decision now is Yours."

Tamias remained outwardly composed, though he was afraid that his heart would burst with relief and joy. "No decision is necessary. To become a member of the Zoo-Community has been my long-standing ambition. Thank You for the wonderful opportunity. I will practice the Three Keys of Mastery, Chemistry and Delivery with pride."

"Welcome to Your new home, Tamias!" said Moose.

# Moose's Moxie / The Eleven Laws

*Moose's Law of Meetings:* Customer satisfaction is inversely related to the amount of time spent in meetings.

*Moose's Law of Enlightened Self-Interest:* In order to receive from Your employer, You must first give to Your Customer.

*Moose's Law of Mastery:* Mastery never seeks reward; rewards always find Mastery.

*Moose's Law of Mission:* The only Purpose of organizations is to meet Customers' needs.

*Moose's Law of Solutions:* Complaining makes You part of the problem. Defining successful outcomes makes You part of the solution.

*Moose's Law of Creativity:* Innovation results from building on new ideas, not criticizing them.

*Moose's Law of Listening:* The need for honest listening rises with seniority.

*Moose's Law of Recruitment:* Superstars are not selected by organizations; organizations are selected by superstars.

*Moose's Law of Bureaucracy:* In an organization

enjoying a rising tide of happy Customers, administration is a secondary function.

*Moose's Law of Leadership:* A successful team with one hundred members has one hundred leaders.

*Moose's Law of Assets:* Superior organizations possess only two major assets: employees and Customers. All other assets automatically follow.

## The Seven Skills of the Trainer

- Criticize constructively and *never* criticize the new ideas of others; instead, build on them.

- Pay attention to complaints.

- Keep everyone informed and respect their right and need to know.

- Learn to be respected rather than liked.

- Ask Your subordinates for their advice and help.

- Develop a sense of responsibility in Your subordinates and expect the same thing from Your peers.

- Emphasize *Mastery* rather than *rules*.

# The Seven Laws of Listening

- Develop a *listening attitude*.

- Go to an appropriate relaxed environment, conducive to attentive listening.

- Avoid interruptions, distractions and power signals.

- Clear the mind; focus on the objectives of the exchange.

- Prepare an agenda.

- Don't guess ahead.

- Restate what you heard.

## TO CONTINUE FOLLOWING
## THE WAY OF THE TIGER

Lance H.K. Secretan speaks to conventions and organizations all over the world. His messages are also available on audio and video tape.

In addition, Dr. Secretan conducts workshops, retreats and in-depth consulting on strategic vision, leadership, entrepreneurship and corporate spirit and culture.

Also available is **THE PERSONAL MASTER-CLASS**—a personal workbook based on *The Way of the Tiger*. It is designed to assist You to reflect more deeply on some of the ideas contained in this book so that You can apply them to Your own life in a practical way, and by doing so, refresh and renew Your spirit.

Dr. Secretan is always pleased to hear from his readers. Please write to him at:

*Dr. Lance H.K. Secretan*
*The Thaler Corporation Inc.*
*R.R. #2,*
*Alton, Ontario LON 1A0*
*CANADA*